BLETCHLEYPARK

CRYPTIC CROSSWORDS

BLETCHLEYPARK

This edition was published in 2017 by the Bletchley Park Trust
The Mansion, Bletchley Park, Milton Keynes, MK3 6EB

ISBN: 978-1-78828-043-3
AD005836UK

Cover design by Rose
Printed in the UK

CONTENTS

INTRODUCTION

During World War Two, Bletchley Park was a workplace to thousands of people whose job it was to read the encrypted messages of its enemies. Towards the end of 1941, a crossword puzzle competition was organised by the *Daily Telegraph*. The challenge was to complete the puzzle in under 12 minutes. A Mr Gavin, Chairman of the Eccentrics Club, offered to donate £100 to the Minesweepers Fund, if it could be done under controlled conditions. As a number of the competitors were subsequently invited to take part in intelligence work at Bletchley Park, puzzles and codebreaking have been linked in the public mind ever since the exploits of Bletchley Park's Codebreakers became public knowledge.

Codebreaking is very much a puzzle-solving process and the codes and ciphers used are similar to the most common types of puzzles such as crosswords, wordsearches and sudoku. In many cases, the Codebreakers of Bletchley Park were looking for patterns in the problem before them, much like puzzle solvers today. Both often also base their solutions on clues. For example, a simple code might represent words by something else such as strings of numbers. In this case, the clue may lie in the frequency of certain strings of numbers occurring in the encrypted message. Straight or quick crossword clues are simple definitions of the answers, so the clue lies in the definition provided. A more difficult cipher might replace each letter in a message with another letter of the alphabet twice, a so-called double-encryption. This is a bit like cryptic crosswords in which the clues are puzzles in themselves.

Encrypted World War Two enemy messages were usually transmitted in groups of letters, typically 4 or 5 in length. So when the letters were decrypted, they would still be in these letter groups but some letters might be missing. The Codebreakers would then have to piece the actual words of the message together. This is a bit like a 'fill-in-the-blank' clue in crosswords or wordsearch puzzles.

So you see, puzzle solving is synonymous with the profound intellectual feat and remarkable brains of those whose work at Bletchley Park is said to have helped shorten World War Two by up to two years. Following in this long-held tradition, the Bletchley Park Trust has today produced this series of puzzle books so that you can follow in the footsteps of the Codebreakers and perhaps establish whether you have the puzzle-solving skills needed to have worked at wartime Bletchley Park...

Across

1 He's in unrivalled command (6)
4 Salad for an emperor? (6)
9 None was heard for prayer? (3)
10 Extra, we hear, noticed about line in computing trend (6,3)
11 Idea's wasted in private comment (5)
12 Place in wild for bird (7)
14 Fault of contrived author, riveting work largely ruined? (11)
17 Fruit from a tropic is cultivated (7)
18 Lifted section of floor is enamelled (5)
20 Amphibian's drill, perhaps, creates fungi (9)
22 Garland male in boxing (3)
23 Friendly touch in a sort of film (6)
24 My pug's chewed soft mineral (6)

Down

1 Bar around some fig tree (6)
2 Language behind Indian houses (5)
3 Having exact correspondence? (9)
5 Outstanding airman (3)
6 Fossil, I conclude, holds metalloid (7)
7 Argue with anonymous tree (5)
8 English in confined space getting share in assistance (11)
13 Inspired European meeting with precision (9)
15 Very short song not lacking heart? It's different (7)
16 Popular company devoid of strength (6)
17 Malfunction in part of play increased (3,2)
19 Speak of people and fish (5)
21 Do wrong in cursing (3)

Across

1 Snap good English architect (5)
4 Joined cats? (7)
9 Rug meant for repair producing row (8)
10 Take interior image of unknown fish (1-3)
11 Advice's misplaced ignoring depth in bladder (6)
12 I pulse for a gold, maybe? (5)
13 Pitt, perhaps, is born 'Most Excellent' (4)
15 Thanks daughter a bit (3)
16 South African mountain that floats in the sea? (4)
17 It carries current article on poetic work (5)
19 Coaches, vehicles on rails (6)
21 Leading asterisk (4)
22 Bothers with problems (8)
23 Letters edited in framework (7)
24 Amid Spanish cheers, leader of group stares impertinently (5)

Down

2 Bravery in prisoner vehicle (5)
3 Horse-breeding establishment that is deserted is examined (7)
5 Intelligence department in hint making use of threats (12)
6 Socialized in diverse fashion? (5)
7 Less substantial shopping area in series (7)
8 Separate chaps tense in agreement regarding division at work? (12)
14 Priest accepting a nuclear facility (7)
16 Seat constructed from legume, black and silver (7)
18 Some retrogressive monstrous types (5)
20 Relative's lovely, full of energy (5)

3

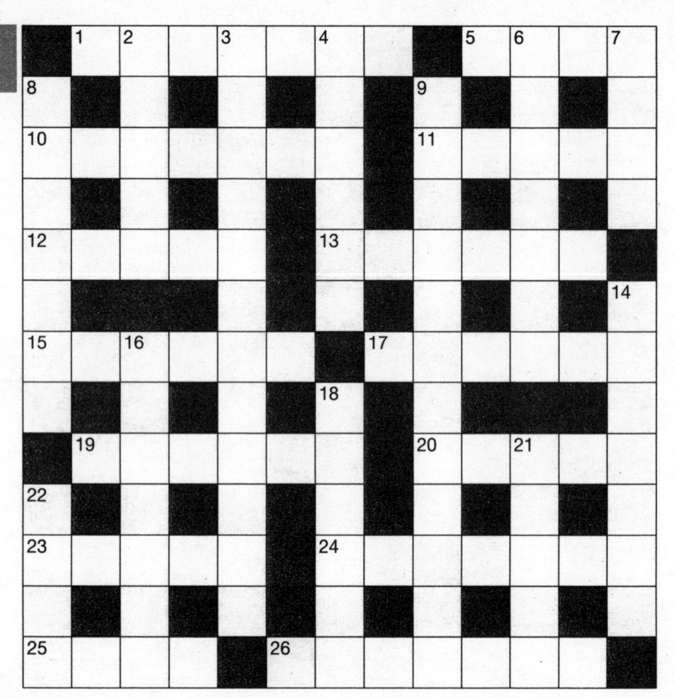

Across

1 European gentleman carrying winding rope, one in supreme control (7)
5 I study carefully venerated figure (4)
10 Energy at the back of the Chinese? (7)
11 I love name in charge of classical order (5)
12 Irritate loudspeaker without tenor (5)
13 Negative response is drugs disturbances, perhaps (6)
15 Lined up with one currently touring Arkansas (2,1,3)
17 Also a dandy? (2,4)
19 Light illness with very loud yawn at start (6)
20 Women in matches not starting journeys (5)
23 Shift stolen goods in pen (5)
24 Delicate paper put in dossier (7)
25 Remains, it's said, in an underworld river (4)
26 One favouring the cream in English literature? It's fantastic (7)

Down

2 Subatomic particle thus located among fellows (5)
3 Occasionally, envy of stereo goes crazy! (5,2,5)
4 Having eccentric in gown (6)
6 Admit case against top player, we hear (7)
7 Lovely French city (4)
8 Oceanic games delay 99 (7)
9 TV vicar's line troubled public administrator (5,7)
14 Place flower patch (7)
16 A fast yacht principally retaining power a lot (7)
18 A Parisian landmark, you say? That's a lot to look at! (6)
21 Doctor beginning to inspect extra note for fluid devices (5)
22 On holiday, sun kills (4)

Across

1 Rough agent behind artist (5)
4 Ridicules firm with fine fellow on board (6)
10 In front of church, busy car lane is emptying (9)
11 Ate three notes (3)
12 Exert influence over West London suburb (3,2)
13 Stirred up and took away, without right (6)
14 Good English chaps in absolute order (11)
18 Fall into the habit of something at the second attempt, say (4,2)
20 Special address to queen showing oiliness (5)
23 Employ Sue haphazardly (3)
24 Guilty parties get these groups of words (9)
25 Tests material among Rastas say stupidly (6)
26 Allow a degree by US college (5)

Down

2 Warning – beer with rubbish taste for starters (5)
3 Old man seen round country hotel, swimmer with notorious reputation? (7)
5 County embracing radical set of beliefs (5)
6 Guidance for viewing on screens, perhaps, with first tennis point (7)
7 Team expressed yearning, we hear (4)
8 Very thin figure namely with newspaper (5)
9 Illegal position of mine? (11)
15 University lecturers? They're sought by writers (7)
16 Wild dreams about India interpreted wrongly (7)
17 US sect going wrong under the influence of drink? (5)
19 Student's work in Spain and Sweden, for example (5)
21 Leaders in a scientific company install internet digital letter code (inits) (5)
22 Feeling in reformed drinkers around old city (4)

Across

1 Higher fort's maintenance (6)
5 Learner in a university mistook man as former female student (6)
8 Release from confinement without cost (4)
9 The West has mishap with nothing replacing America (8)
10 Bard idly relaxed seeing beetle (8)
11 Ancient city's not right for childish items (4)
12 Key outburst (6)
14 Don possibly to fall asleep (3,3)
16 Ruler in court's arbitrary (4)
18 A soft mother or father is obvious (8)
20 Mixture of nice, poor sheep's cheese (8)
21 Good attention in outfit (4)
22 Dine in north-east getting new order (6)
23 Say lie glibly and effortlessly (6)

Down

2 Person with instruments right off, maybe (7)
3 Each always by yard (5)
4 Review of inertial proof showing rapid increase (13)
5 Decrepit canon slipping is liable to mishaps (8-5)
6 Modernized upper-class pad vandalized by unruly youth (7)
7 African politics in New York and French city (5)
13 Area left round Irish travel hub (7)
15 Cool man, it's said, having communication from admirer? (3,4)
17 Northern European vegetable (5)
19 Gets stormy in nameless mountains (5)

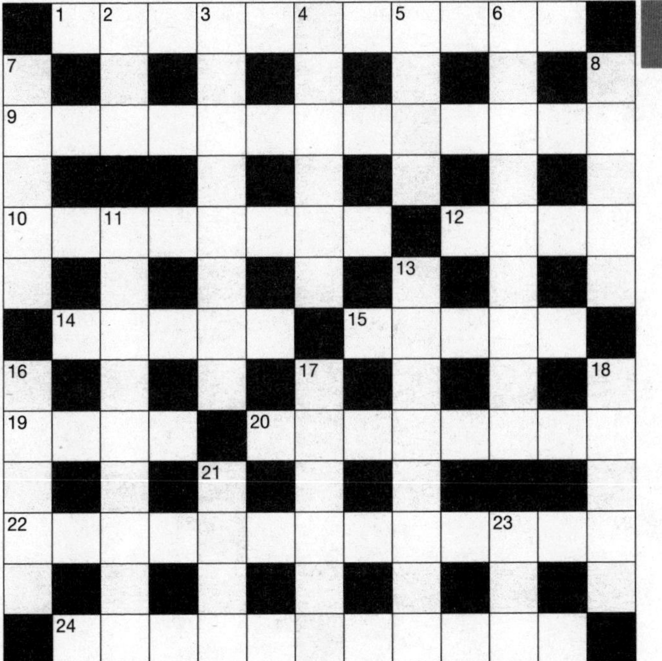

Across

1 Large sandwiches a Latin chomped after time (11)
9 A book found in Scottish island before speech, joint work (13)
10 Global body knowing about broadcast improperly (8)
12 Burden facing America (4)
14 Flattens clubs (5)
15 Note drill with energy in tent (5)
19 Approve old area in Kentucky (4)
20 Former contractor Edward shortly is due (8)
22 Understand say returning motifs in stage works (3,3,7)
24 Fresh ratings dive for promotional campaign (11)

Down

2 Some amateur loser in online location (inits) (3)
3 Posts in railway buildings? (8)
4 A head, head of office, handsome young man (6)
5 Take exotic wood (4)
6 Lamenting organized alliance (9)
7 Get rid of stunted growth (5)
8 Anxiety among gangsters (5)
11 Arranged for LeBlanc to join journalist (9)
13 See laser deployed in films made public (8)
16 Evade American car (5)
17 Free vote supported by English politician in film (6)
18 Extra promotion with note put on edition (5)
21 Tough eel hides butter (4)
23 All went normally at first for bristle-like growth (3)

Across

1 Bewilder graduate with fine set of papers I overlooked (6)
5 Lessen wine on cue possibly (6)
8 Token feature of astrology? (4)
9 General survey about six we backed (8)
10 Unusual clue put in Northern Ireland centres (6)
11 Rise, go out, revamp (6)
12 TV prize, prize judge omitted (4)
14 Number linked to West currently (3)
15 Whirlpool with headless toy bear (4)
16 Films etc in US city getting setback regarding stars? (6)
18 Admit prince is deadly (6)
20 Coins are exchanged in plan of action (8)
22 Freshwater fish for Australian PM (4)
23 Mistaken rule defended by following journalist (6)
24 Hole? It is shifted for implement (6)

Down

2 A duke that is posh bidding farewell (5)
3 Colleague put behind arm in the end (7)
4 English poet with a line that's moving (9)
5 Propel boat, I hear, to find fish eggs (3)
6 Divorced press leader descended steeply (5)
7 Defrauded companion spilt tea over journalist (7)
11 Diplomatic reception that's not desirable (9)
13 Cats, say, of a noted quality? (7)
15 Hold spellbound characters in umpteenth rally (7)
17 Invigorate French man with wife (5)
19 'Check gold', said in French (5)
21 Free right I initially deny (3)

8

Across

1 Rates educational groups (7)
5 Possible style in deaf Roman (4)
9 Main pit dug over with drums (7)
10 Jobs for Poles? (5)
11 The Spanish had a meal to cheer up (5)
12 Some seven lyricists in uniform style (6)
14 Spin is working for jail (6)
16 Trainee doctor partly exhumed icosahedron (6)
18 Roused a doyen at some point (3,3)
19 Petite fellow in westerly river (5)
22 Cruise perhaps starts to amuse chirpy tourists on Rhine (5)
23 Bird of prey in strait seen in part of ship (7)
24 Heading off reforms ambitions (4)
25 Heard tales about floors (7)

Down

2 Premise in liberal novel (5)
3 Hero stalked possibly one with concern in business (11)
4 Left former sex appeal, perhaps, with editor (6)
6 With ado, almost ill, one type of pasta (7)
7 Expel leader missing in tournament (4)
8 Endeavour in agency worker attorney retains (7)
10 Former figure about to get into varied seed crops (11)
13 Together with happiness, hugged internal labourer first (7)
15 Faulty editing is lit up (7)
17 Fool touring yard with mark in athletic gear (3,3)
20 Vehicle made of iron runs on railway (5)
21 Trap silver in church (4)

Across

8 Name only varies in material (5)
9 Suspension in display of paintings (7)
10 Talk about man to an audience for fast transfer? (7)
11 Shadow seen in glum branch (5)
12 Leader in oil I rated wrongly (9)
14 Right, district attorney, that's enough for one day! (inits) (3)
15 Brit's cleaner back (3)
16 Merrymaking not right with a police force? It's evident in leafy vegetables (5,4)
19 Inexperienced environmental activist (5)
21 New large quantity in pasta strips (7)
23 Object to performance that's disgusting (7)
24 I sell broken stocking material (5)

Down

1 Enter novel idea about Nevada (6)
2 Convoluted rituals might at first create selflessness (8)
3 Peruvian, say, favoured California (4)
4 Hot dish or cold one (6)
5 At a tavern left in charge openly (2,6)
6 Arm, say, group of climbers (4)
7 One fruit replaces five with new lizard (6)
13 Criminal's not working with drinking binge – headless! (8)
14 Some freckles suspected to be rash (8)
15 Source of bacon over a long time – and bird (6)
17 Secured like an aristocrat? (6)
18 Touches and scuttles! (6)
20 Relaxed with a piece of cake (4)
22 Cries without hard birds (4)

10

Across

7 Window location in study, perhaps (7)
9 Gynaecologist covers in review body of water (5)
10 Cuter naked Native American (3)
11 Planning a royal hunt? (9)
12 A pinch of contact? (5)
14 Likes better official in a society (7)
16 Clash taking place in ill-disciplined side (7)
18 South American greeting Japanese dish (5)
19 Flight one covered in brilliant action (9)
20 Insolence in kiss? (3)
21 A long period recalled in stadium (5)
22 Teacher holding varied mail in uniform (7)

Down

1 Now fair, editor changed (8)
2 Key part of supermarket, it's said (4)
3 Add after a time volunteers with church (6)
4 Resilience in short man at door of club (6)
5 Dwellers in studies surrounding one branch of Buddhism (8)
6 Comfortable retracting firearms (4)
8 Rewiring helps repair computer hardware (11)
13 Implicit condition in United Nations declaration principally (8)
15 Like indoor footwear without friction? (8)
17 Like a poor book under a mongrel (6)
18 Garland made from stone and book (6)
19 Charts brought up meat product (4)
20 Cheerful song inspired around 50 (4)

Across

1 Lens setting with loud finish (1-4)
4 US helicopter swiftly circling hospital (6)
10 Slow, say, consume and collapse (5,4)
11 Conditions regularly diffuse (3)
12 Congressman returns after six – spiteful person! (5)
13 Soft bed for sportsman (6)
14 I steer divas distressed with difficulties (11)
18 Supplement at home taken with rest possibly (6)
20 Protective cloth by the French Holy Book (5)
23 Old game minimally maintained (3)
24 Varied seed crops subjected to treatment (9)
25 Bring to ground and nail the French (6)
26 Two people return for award in Italian cathedral (5)

Down

2 Search curved drive in front of building (5)
3 Retake again after nothing bears fruit? (3,4)
5 Black and white animal and hugged by father (5)
6 See ground behind prominent feature of an Asian race? (7)
7 Gaelic language in poetry needing no introduction (4)
8 Sailor, almost over and higher (5)
9 Music's ingredients? (11)
15 Powerful explosive, with carbon replacing tellurium (7)
16 Greek character takes in accomplished diorama (7)
17 Socially inept sorts in North East streets (5)
19 Get rid of spreadsheet software, softly replacing 100 (5)
21 Son cut pole on ship in one's clasp (5)
22 One in the dark missing line (4)

Across

1 A charming accent (5)
4 Ecuador has bad logo with chromosome for biological field (7)
9 Special beers by guy in pitcher? (8)
10 One mother is a religious leader (4)
11 More is developed as substance of identical weight (6)
12 Moved gradually getting advantage on day (5)
13 Feature of fish in small measure (4)
15 Person left out tiny amount of money (3)
16 Trapped in business function? (4)
17 Long period of time before November (5)
19 Head food? (6)
21 A liberal with money, source of spectacular charitable relief (4)
22 He's one of them, chaps wearing sort of steel (8)
23 Clear film in great London gallery (7)
24 Tree like a swan (5)

Down

2 Warm clothing that could be put on by painters? (5)
3 Warm Frenchman in unusual lather (7)
5 Ends in game assuming no prior knowledge (12)
6 Prone to duplicity (5)
7 Delight boy engaged in good study (7)
8 Being put in a stir? (12)
14 Trouble recalled in curiously dicy characteristic of pastoral work? (7)
16 Demonstrators in quick rainfall (7)
18 Advantage in property (5)
20 Literally, that man is supple (5)

13

Across

6 Guru's pupil with revolutionary and the French (5)
7 Travel behind river in a profound way (6)
9 Brynner has electronic record for festive cake (4,3)
10 Speech therefore showing authority (3-2)
11 Carve new tech (4)
13 Colt and also-ran nearer (6)
15 Cut tiny quantity of satirical work (5)
16 Infer first sign of defeat in tennis score (6)
17 Supranational unit in unfinished building complex (4)
20 Deal strangely to include large spoon (5)
22 I stream about conductors (7)
23 A tall grass I obliterated second is surprising (6)
24 In the middle of day with silver lining (5)

Down

1 Agent severely reprimanded and supplanted (8)
2 First sign of seafaring troubles in journeys on water (5)
3 Saying herded by Canada geese (5)
4 Reflexively she helps Santa, perhaps, with Dasher's hind half section in front (7)
5 Colleague that's friendly doffing cap (4)
6 Bonnie's partner leads stray horse (10)
8 Putting right element in my park beginning to grate (10)
12 Copy primate (3)
13 Element of machinery in firm close to failing (3)
14 Loot in US dispersed? It provides answer to problem (8)
15 Special singer with curtailed zoo movement (7)
18 In the morning, employ and entertain (5)
19 Summary about headwear (5)
21 Wet barrier on top of pool (4)

Across

1 It's among developments initially behind a motorway (4)
4 Striking appearances as prospects (8)
8 Lively wit in unorthodox priest (6)
9 Give up rule limiting sun (6)
10 Bachelor jogged for food (4)
11 Crave tie, dreadfully artistic (8)
13 Distasteful thing, a bin Leo vandalized (13)
16 Alphabet lyric in a mess with three numbers (8)
19 Small amount of money abroad transmitted, we hear (4)
20 Unexpected study backing south of France (6)
22 First person's criticism limited for spiritual figure (6)
23 Setbacks in driving manoeuvres (8)
24 Moved fast among ponderous pedestrians (4)

Down

2 Aim Beryl's devised in gloomy fashion (9)
3 Angered, agitated, make insane (7)
4 Operation tense, with initially infectious conjunctivitis related to the eye (5)
5 Poor Ted mishandled naval weapon (7)
6 Beginning where film is shot? (5)
7 Barrel found in Lake Geneva (3)
12 Event in ground in which one gets a large romantic card (9)
14 Scouts seek them, stories about holy books (7)
15 Charges a cricket club employs (7)
17 At home, long for non-mainstream music label (5)
18 Fasteners left out in tented areas (5)
21 Leaders in unconventional alliance exasperate Arab country (inits) (3)

Across

7 Gold wise men return with one art of paper folding (7)
9 Alien's after October group (5)
10 Desperate character getting level of proficiency in martial sport (3)
11 Sign showing Italian island produce (9)
12 Poster on NI party has to make sense (3,2)
14 Favoured old boy told a story about gravity (7)
16 Implement nurse with strength (7)
18 Brings home drinks containers, we hear (5)
19 Poster son moved for kitchen tidy (5,4)
20 Gas has no borders, making fuss (3)
21 Bear a tender sore ultimately (5)
22 Dramatic work in place for operations? (7)

Down

1 Seeing red in a way? (4,4)
2 Look that is found in Minnesota (4)
3 Hothead puts a type of electricity in atlas page? (6)
4 In this way spies left party (6)
5 More competent sort of gents – or luckier ultimately (8)
6 Hit rising almonds, for instance (4)
8 Men move trip after organizing upgrade (11)
13 Swimming area following craze on reflection for flower (8)
15 Find inspector's top? (8)
17 Messy diners washed (6)
18 One of two, I was in the clear air (6)
19 Cast a glance, ensnaring deer (4)
20 Skills in roles quietly discarded (4)

Across

1 Rubbish eaten as a fruit? (7)
5 Deep chasm in area near ship (5)
9 Hit one foreign badly about (2,3,6,2)
10 District supporting senior Liberal Democrat familiarly? (8)
11 Submissive writer, English knight (4)
12 British person put forward with unknown bravado (9)
16 Contented sound that's partly interrupted from the rear (4)
17 Lodge with artist in check (8)
19 Survey journey north in Hebridean island taken with passion (13)
21 On the radio, want to massage (5)
22 Homer's adventure? (7)

Down

2 European country ignoring area starved of resources (6)
3 Conduct I have misjudged amid stench over old city (9)
4 US medical drama in series, a programme shown again (5)
6 Voice disapproval of limited volume (3)
7 Made a point and made a scratch (6)
8 Accords with breaking down grease (6)
11 Most wary manoeuvring round old major routes (9)
13 Allow hairstyle with appeal (6)
14 Fall for Virginia? (6)
15 If returning, Queen and church are vicious (6)
18 Bad thing, say, to overdose in Church assembly (5)
20 Ask about musical style (3)

Across

1 £1000 payments covering old man and aged relatives (12)
8 First lady enters lines in uniform (5)
9 Exalted side cut short meal (4,3)
10 Browse first parts of series using rare footage (4)
11 Clingy companion in farm building, one fringing lake (8)
14 Ancient silver lode produced (3-3)
15 Scottish football team in a suit? (6)
17 Steadily, across the calendar (3,2,3)
18 Repeated denial is not acceptable (2-2)
20 Restore miracle to return to former glory (7)
22 Noted middle-distance runner beginning to prevent muscular pain (5)
23 Diligence succeeded in job requests (12)

Down

1 Greece's first ancient flag and monetary system (4,8)
2 Deal's very corrupt in contrary fashion (9)
3 Side line crosses meat counter (4)
4 Sheep under tree in religious retreat (6)
5 Manoeuvre shown by constructive type (8)
6 Add a small child (3)
7 Hard as soap, Bruce ordered a summons (6,6)
12 Food ingredient feasible with a party? It's beef stew (9)
13 Co-operate in dramatic event before dance (4,4)
16 River rodent rises on a road surface (6)
19 Leave southern California beginning to tremble (4)
21 Chump oddly gets ornamental trophy (3)

Across

7 Some bring a tea untold cake (6)
8 I boost nervous musician (6)
9 Cross swiftly with hundred in the south of France (4)
10 Ambitious person, good working together, not hard (2-6)
11 Awkward – he held booby strangely (11)
14 Ultimate traffic congestion wrecked experts (11)
18 Communications from wise figure amid chaos (8)
19 Credit electronic Western group (4)
20 Withdraw from work and trade (3,3)
21 Dashes around four-poster and encloses snugly (6)

Down

1 Study covering irregular chat to become fashionable (5,2)
2 Notice day as source of growth (4)
3 Girl discontented in period of summer in dense forest (6)
4 Switch to Google without glasses? (6)
5 Delay job open to change (8)
6 According to friendly ghost... no head! (2,3)
12 Source of volume on the high street? (8)
13 Goes to stated criminal hiding name (7)
15 Deny Geordie scandal? (6)
16 Procedure confused my sets (6)
17 Entice casual worker with first of treats (5)
19 Young animals in some cards left out (4)

Across

1 Playful cat? Sit still! (6)
5 Friend by outstanding royal abode (6)
8 Animal hands back exchange (4)
9 Commander surrounded by more modern beginner (8)
10 Fall over the French three times! (6)
11 Save, secure somehow (6)
12 Argument after central character disappears in downfall (4)
14 Finally not against small screens (abbr) (3)
15 Fine American warship in commotion (4)
16 Money lender university is more certain (6)
18 Disney holds Greek letter for wood (6)
20 Sort of talc seen to be most hygienic (8)
22 Fine piece of cheese, ricotta (4)
23 Students cutting university education not employed? (6)
24 Is knight in colour exposed to danger? (6)

Down

2 Fortification to stand high (5)
3 Pressure amid uncertain points – feature of tennis? (7)
4 Alternating to direct device and preacher, possibly (9)
5 Scrape chess piece endlessly (3)
6 See son holding acceptable views (5)
7 Revolutionary massages angelic types (7)
11 Wear and store new-fangled perfume (4,5)
13 Particle increases state with zero number (7)
15 Fine society keeping more ancient directories (7)
17 Studies article probing radicals (5)
19 Join army division close to battle (5)
21 Stop ambition (3)

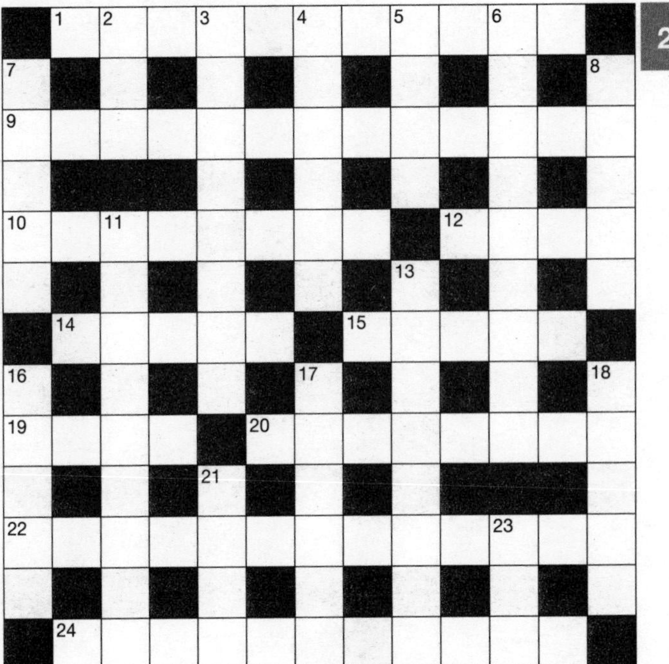

Across

1 Tender peers in play given depiction (11)
9 First person's relation? (13)
10 Lives with sandwich, and nuns lacking hesitation (8)
12 Measure of drink restricted emotional episode (4)
14 Capable of enduring difficult conditions with Thomas? (5)
15 See a couple of directions for financial transactions (5)
19 Prefer to dissemble about king (4)
20 Revolutionary book is about old Nationalist showing feelings (8)
22 A pressure on support I found in short supply for money set aside (13)
24 Sort among radios, maybe, showing conventional images (11)

Down

2 Put away some baggage attentively (3)
3 Constructs again the Italian diagram initially seen in puzzle (8)
4 Polished host possibly entertaining medical officer (6)
5 Socially inept person in corner disowned (4)
6 Neat prose crafted in artificial language (9)
7 Produce inducement (5)
8 Short person in unusual gym in quiet yard (5)
11 Bachelor misses trophy in troublesome place (5,4)
13 Leave unreliable dates over year to enjoy secure relationship (2,6)
16 Seaweed blown in a gale (5)
17 Foetus developed by Rome (6)
18 Enjoying American variety of gin (5)
21 Dull day round old city (4)
23 Father shunning son in anger (3)

Across

1 Get to know again relative near ground (7)
5 Fetch almost close to shore salty water (5)
9 Comical points possibly in medical setbacks? (13)
10 Uneducated number I allow outside (8)
11 Steal child's bed (4)
12 Important street has vermin, for example, in charge (9)
16 Arkansas has inhospitable desert, primarily very dry (4)
17 Varied leaders touring Catholic states (8)
19 Tot feeling bed awkwardly? Means to supply one liquid (7,6)
21 Quantity of drugs in chest as hoped (5)
22 Gibe unfortunately scars a Frenchman (7)

Down

2 One hug sadly is sufficient (6)
3 Former policeman holding scruffy tie is taken advantage of (9)
4 Camera I take captures Indian dish (5)
6 Russia regularly develops pain after continuous use (inits) (3)
7 Sister with chapter I love is papal ambassador (6)
8 Shed left by European fortification (6)
11 Like weather conditions in which there's cold as a culmination? (9)
13 Helping and looting without leader (6)
14 Stripe disturbed minister (6)
15 King arranged meals in kingdoms (6)
18 Firm support for government committee (5)
20 Correct actions for old IBM PC? (3)

Across

1 Take heed of a brew drunk close to village (6)
4 A metabolic disease I found in rodent (6)
8 Rock concealing river fish (3)
9 Engaging English politician somewhat sickly? Not at first (9)
11 Catch sight of online agent? (4)
12 Creates dark perhaps pleasures (8)
15 Constant criminal and others around university (9)
18 Contaminates mixed company, King spews without energy (8)
19 Stumble in journey (4)
21 Trade, say, altered after European feast (6,3)
23 Single component in honesty (3)
24 Old, old tax is too much (6)
25 Count Anglicans taken with northern and southern America (6)

Down

1 Queen, say, dined and grumbled (6)
2 Bland background, something in Berlin daily? (9)
3 Jagged rock concealed by tree firstly (4)
5 Magnificent slug exploded about old Brazilian city (8)
6 International body with one college (3)
7 Eat as a joke, we hear (6)
10 Existing eating disorder is introduced (9)
13 Very funny hour I sail at sea (9)
14 Sort sure to change lower body wear (8)
16 Project in school on East and Middle East (6)
17 Awake, prepares unexpected victories (6)
20 Part of car to wear out, we're told (4)
22 Dry moment (3)

23

Across

8 Deny validity to a Greek character in the Netherlands (5)
9 First thing before surname? (7)
10 Concept still seen with time (7)
11 I study time for distinctive channel sequence (5)
12 Fish surrounding nasty energy to have freedom of movement (4,3,2)
14 Heartless young animal next to head of snake for American network (inits) (3)
15 The Italian lecturer is off-colour (3)
16 Ministerial responsibility left by fool I fancy (9)
19 Modify feature of church, we hear (5)
21 Milk substitute's equation (7)
23 A horse with tail in various sizes (7)
24 First of police called in crash (5)

Down

1 Strategy to reverse breath mint? (6)
2 Where one might find student, a learner that's relaxed (8)
3 Block with a shoe (4)
4 Shook to a particular size (6)
5 Become friendly in Caribbean island taking out a posh type (3,2,3)
6 Naked maiden is an assistant (4)
7 Staple cooking in dishes (6)
13 Partisan strangely is ambitious (8)
14 Sect posh artist left regarding arts and the like? (8)
15 Favourite holidaying to some extent (2,1,3)
17 Decline to accept rubbish (6)
18 Love scope in fruit (6)
20 Stole kilo under also (4)
22 Businessmen concerned with extra note (4)

24

Across

7 USA hits broken Japanese therapy (7)
9 Drive? No! Going nowhere at this speed! (5)
10 Court sports body is large, thanks (inits) (3)
11 Spoil Mother, deal out jam (9)
12 Label wheels that are forbidden (5)
14 A titled figure mentioned in story (7)
16 A new leading girl in dress for Indian instrument (7)
18 Visionary harbouring new cynical expression (5)
19 Like one with a complaint? (9)
20 Cat near mouse initially (3)
21 Attractive figure with little twang (5)
22 Reviewers credit second part of film with spasms (7)

Down

1 Disconnects one signal for help, covering dead (8)
2 Former currency in collateral I raised (4)
3 A poet freely keeping month for musical instruction (1,5)
4 Work of coloured marble regarding Jewish law (6)
5 Small measure excited a true green (8)
6 Part of gift he endowed to you, of old (4)
8 Impractical cartel in US I disbanded (11)
13 Bunk on a ship, say, period for celebration (8)
15 It is a rum mixed dessert (8)
17 Tale embroidered in US city in adroit fashion (6)
18 Sore about mass international defeat (6)
19 Open top diplomatic party? (4)
20 Can contains Welsh lookalike (4)

25

Across

6 Ascends avoiding first large tree branches (5)
7 Half of characters in charge of a type of power? (6)
9 A dry ale drunk previously (7)
10 Guide on boat missing right source of milk (5)
11 Long fish in drums right away (4)
13 Unites in summer, gesticulating (6)
15 Mislays first of leaflets on sales event soon (5)
16 Declare rupee ancient coin (6)
17 Fasten river floor (4)
20 Independent spot surrounds one fool (5)
22 Happiness from turning off a lamp? (7)
23 Vegetable and barrel returns with legume (6)
24 Trumpet beginning to deafen mob (5)

Down

1 Handy protection against downfall? (8)
2 Test arsenic for example (5)
3 Stray sadly with lecherous figure (5)
4 Pieces stirring old muse (7)
5 Prepare for American soldier, King and daughter (4)
6 Heard spiel misrepresented as authority? (10)
8 Following sign of age, criminal trade gets thwarted (10)
12 Number taken with Republican – or neither! (3)
13 Fellows from Middle East and Norway (3)
14 Stupid person importing varied gins in suspect activity (6-2)
15 Allowing a property renting (7)
18 Changes orders without hint of certainty (5)
19 Notice time-keeping piece (5)
21 Decorated a cake ascending at the beginning of the last month (4)

26

Across

1 Most eminent saint behind tree (5)
4 Son checks bonds (6)
10 Good-for-nothing, namely friend with footballer's partner (9)
11 Fool overturned can (3)
12 Part of denial I bind is proof of innocence (5)
13 Simpler English eras I fancy (6)
14 Presenting new conduit ring (11)
18 Lecturer with different title is insignificant (6)
20 Black Earl, skeletal (5)
23 Noted female singer in monochrome (3)
24 Panic! Moon transformed friend (9)
25 Confine oneself to fortified area with pair, we hear (4,2)
26 Incomplete hermit rose with open sore (5)

Down

2 Independent artist facing leading question, an Arab (5)
3 Unwell, tucked in, rise confused feeling more stupid (7)
5 Article in clothing, garments draped on Romans (5)
6 Business worry (7)
7 Badger's burrow found in Dorset trail (4)
8 Customary American university area with lake (5)
9 Visions of candy for the best thoughts! (5,6)
15 Offensive feeling rises, with ultimate disgust replaced by sadness initially (7)
16 Line with shout, we hear? It's part of snooker (3,4)
17 Struggling and surveying, but not sure (5)
19 Unspoken agreement a citizen sealed (5)
21 It's nothing to be a Mediterranean fruit (5)
22 Shake tower of strength (4)

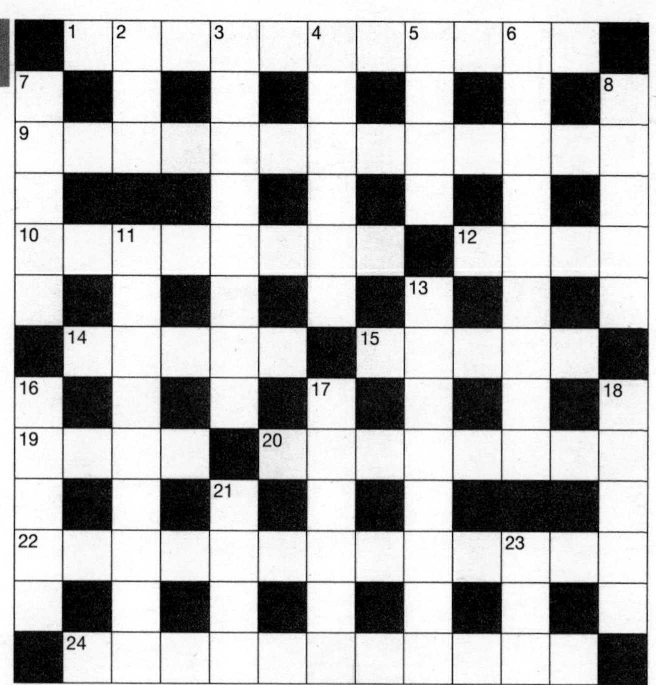

Across

1 Gibberish from a supporter doubly defending dishonourable type (11)
9 Therapists treating coy pigs and sloths (13)
10 Noted male on chest in grass (8)
12 Idiot found upside down in hodgepodge (4)
14 Favoured rental property is sound (5)
15 Shake off puzzle! (5)
19 Drinks for children? (4)
20 Implanted and slept with them before (8)
22 A march in Peru devised around lake needing protected illumination (9,4)
24 Teaching ace duo Latin for a change (11)

Down

2 Sound of dog and horse (3)
3 Bishop in a hard order possibly hated (8)
4 One peels back in the land of Nod (6)
5 Aquatic organism found in natural gas (4)
6 Replied about small pond with east depth (9)
7 Revolved around King reject (5)
8 Headless girls are fools (5)
11 Tracked rector in surprising demotion (9)
13 Different personality damaged large toe (5,3)
16 Uncomfortable, small and headless (5)
17 Miscreant with deed having effect (6)
18 Customize a point about US prosecutor (5)
21 Element of fizz in coke (4)
23 Ceremonial dance first off has this other name (inits) (3)

Across

8 Cook mostly hot stuff as foreign dessert (7)
9 Prophet and a university mentor cut short (5)
10 Bear part of ground (5)
11 Rear circle in inn recalled (5,2)
12 Welshman trapped in swamp and middle of mud for a long time – this speaks volumes without words (4,8)
16 Classic novel is to the point, enjoyed at first with new mug of beer (12)
20 Worker taking in nice ground that's well advanced (7)
23 Capital has ordinary Shakespearean character (5)
24 Era is wrong for increase in pay (5)
25 Creatures in cults (7)

Down

1 Inflated award in the Home Counties? (5)
2 US state revitalized a look about hospital – Massachusetts? (8)
3 English novelist retaining line barely (6)
4 Boast about clothing (4)
5 Compassionate consultant's first with a call (6)
6 Turn in silver in excited eagerness (4)
7 Insipid type getting day round gym fell? (7)
13 A new Navy girl (3)
14 A chum possibly penning piece that's unreasonable (1,3,4)
15 A fine fellow publicizes romantic intrigues (7)
17 Zoo worker who doesn't like penalties? (6)
18 Bird disease? (6)
19 Fail to keep wheel rattling (5)
21 Inca upset noted killer (4)
22 Neat car's exterior (4)

29

Across

1 Democrat wearing almost mad scarf (7)
5 Objections over counterfoil (4)
9 Tire car part (7)
10 Appreciate joke in US city with disgusted expression (5)
11 Information initially outsourced on a city in Italy (5)
12 Source of drink taken by a US lawyer in country (6)
14 Desire outdoor pool with one bachelor inside (6)
16 Yes, Spanish make a mistake with a mountain range (6)
18 Male cuts with perfect exactness round fruit (6)
19 Wandering figure getting pain say discontented (5)
22 Rock musician Ronnie's in clubs (5)
23 Voter in the Spanish city next to hill (7)
24 Conspiratorial men? (4)
25 English seabird on a lake is ceaseless (7)

Down

2 Blanched like chicken (5)
3 Possibly damns absurd noisy music (4,3,4)
4 Observe demand for undiluted drink? (6)
6 Shout out to end hurt and confusion (7)
7 Asian currency backed in hot habitat (4)
8 Plant we get set to appear in Iowa (7)
10 Part of plane damaged in grand gale (7,4)
13 People taking brief walk initially among hens (7)
15 A science by studying melted igloo (7)
17 Rat, maybe, runs over hollow (6)
20 Bread, soft and Italian, thanks! (5)
21 Stick with tense hairpiece (4)

30

Across

1 Modern type of coffee with recipe (6)
4 Settle element in rotten campaign (6)
8 Some courtesy kept by us? (3)
9 Killer whale consumes irregular hearts without a group of musicians (9)
11 Takes meal in chairs without sun (4)
12 Sibling follows an alley oddly in detailed examination (8)
15 Rising moons? Cheers! (7,2)
18 Crime ace confused with dessert (3,5)
19 Reptile caught fabulous bird (4)
21 A line placed and apportioned (9)
23 Centre of sixteenth shirt? (3)
24 Angel destroys part of firstborn (6)
25 Saves struggling tosser (6)

Down

1 Expected do bloke disrupted with no final club (6)
2 Source of music learnt but worked upon (9)
3 Noble person's missing first figure revered by Greeks (4)
5 Provokes son? That's gratuitous (8)
6 Skill in ballet say (3)
7 Quietly lift up and exalt (6)
10 Harmonious type of letter (9)
13 Barrier excited opera star (9)
14 Draws by pieces of land (8)
16 Expand and live to an old age, you say? (6)
17 Open account on English ship (6)
20 Correct trend raised (4)
22 Young man is fat right away (3)

Across

7 Florid style in front of roofing over two firms (6)
8 Regime change leads to defector (6)
9 Challenge of French fighter unknown (4)
10 Good man left in team sport largely in conflict (8)
11 Estimate reassessment of auction call (11)
14 A degree gets altered – order of a liberal politician? (11)
18 Begins again painting etc after break (8)
19 Belt and part of sleeve (4)
20 Come back with this key? (6)
21 Bodily fibres in inner vessels (6)

Down

1 Predicted quartet to rise high, we hear (7)
2 Staff put back close to quay sea fish (4)
3 Dug up bone in UFO's silo (6)
4 Sorrow about Greek film (6)
5 Argument among bellringers? (4-4)
6 Very limited law within Turkey's borders (5)
12 Horse box covers lunatic (8)
13 Ate after street church and is really full (7)
15 Royal tirade is wrong (6)
16 Increasing rebellion (6)
17 Yields to top players, we hear (5)
19 Preserve remedy (4)

Across

1 Video accessory showing spider's work by river (6)
4 Metal found in utensil versatile (6)
9 Winning every other public house (3)
10 Students in two universities join together remarkably (9)
11 Inhabitant first off raised old musical (5)
12 Dwindle, not right, and die (7)
14 Details in class into a criminal (11)
17 Actress Glenn favoured to finish sooner (5,2)
18 Try to influence waiting room (5)
20 Commercial group with restriction about new convicts (5,4)
22 Second British rabble (3)
23 A convenience for salesmen (6)
24 Harsh cut before end of service (6)

Down

1 Legal document on monarch for author (6)
2 Stick one circular mark on face (5)
3 Clearly better work of top hairdresser? (1,3,5)
5 Nothing follows one universal note of debt (inits) (3)
6 Cool van crashes in seething place? (7)
7 I'm after river by borders of Hungary to create a poem (5)
8 Entertaining titled woman with conservationists on a lake is key (11)
13 Record feline on a fallen trunk, we hear (9)
15 Recent baby, neat one at play (7)
16 It's extra after another leaving statement (3-3)
17 Pair of firms associated with a hot drink (5)
19 Sweet old doctor in Belgium and Spain (5)
21 Expression of denial in difficulty reported (3)

Across

8 Verse followed by men amid musical frolics (7)
9 Put in ground some plain terminology (5)
10 Not new, thin dart (5)
11 School has even seamless plots (7)
12 Commander placed energy unit next to amateur primarily enjoying Tetris, say (8,4)
16 Is nice if cafe stirs – lacks of ability to produce the desired effect! (12)
20 Favoured switching dates as an alternative (7)
23 Nurse to take action in case to follow (5)
24 A display holder, of course, initially made for a specific purpose (2,3)
25 Make professional contacts in TV organization (7)

Down

1 Fight a bit (5)
2 Subdue some crossover comedians (8)
3 Stop attraction at college (4,2)
4 Goddess is repeated (4)
5 More productive US singer following religious instruction (6)
6 A cat is a very small thing (4)
7 Encountered angry journalist (7)
13 Affection that ladies crave, at first (inits) (3)
14 Dislike amateur edition (8)
15 Fool cutting call that's non-analogue (7)
17 A type of bean language? (6)
18 Produce 90s drug in box (6)
19 Very tiny kerfuffles obscuring insiders for periods of time (5)
21 Note house in trendy London area (4)
22 Hideout with unknown refuse (4)

Across

7 Thursday decays and pushes (7)
9 A financial transaction mentioned without others? (5)
10 Medical officer gains energy with The Simpsons' tavern owner (3)
11 Disagreement right away over a line characterising a novel? (9)
12 See largely restrained pub (5)
14 I see eccentric defending revolutionary fellows, adversaries (7)
16 Venomous creature present in jungle (7)
18 Regions found in the Far East (5)
19 Clear throat, let go of lozenge (5,4)
20 Homer's dad hidden in sofa bed (3)
21 His go is ruined in Japanese chess (5)
22 Abandoned, beheaded and thrown out (7)

Down

1 Bus melts chaotically and falls (8)
2 Road trimmed for large plant (4)
3 American fuel that's refined is advantageous (6)
4 Celebrity touring home gets starvation (6)
5 Clash with Bob, for instance, and cut short drink (8)
6 Part of shoe in list (4)
8 Orchestrate new chocolate cake (11)
13 Fabric made from introductory pants without special tint (8)
15 Debars South American writer gutting diplomats (8)
17 Rogue then in charge of race (6)
18 Wider piece of embroidery needing no introduction (6)
19 Tennis player's money (4)
20 With wife gone, needs workers (4)

35

Across

1 It enables one to dig out suit (5)
4 Reveals alien inception (6)
10 My ten pets strayed in home of older parents? (5,4)
11 Means of saving money in India and South Africa (inits) (3)
12 Pig's home has 51 writing implements (5)
13 Pastry from city haunt (6)
14 London landmark, home of computer game? (5,6)
18 Ambassador Iran mobilized in rupture (6)
20 Alcohol a German imbibed? (5)
23 For starters, that's my intestine... I didn't need to know that! (inits) (3)
24 Office-holder mixed cumin and folded (9)
25 Majestic month (6)
26 Wild dance – marked like a teenager? (5)

Down

2 Pressure facing city careerist, not initially conceited young man (5)
3 Boxing, perhaps, period when the sun is up (7)
5 Up to one in France raising French bed (5)
6 Matching set of cards in start of game (7)
7 Dug start of trench after hot drink (4)
8 Brief time with Irish (5)
9 Rough marble scene is a likeness (11)
15 Old writer drunk gin for a start (7)
16 Liam is strangely cold about a religion (7)
17 We penned nonsense and composed (5)
19 Snail disturbed traps (5)
21 Bird in Greece stripped rebel (5)
22 Tailless mammal in classical portico (4)

36

Across

8 Part of shoe? It gives one a lift (5)
9 Supervised guy got older (7)
10 Reindeer vehicle I half-bought (7)
11 Look at containing rook in bird's nest (5)
12 Clothes for female in union? (9)
14 Christopher shortly in gear (3)
15 Almost broken vehicle (3)
16 Good golf score I'd reported, being of keen sight (5-4)
19 Small collar for laggard (5)
21 A denial about diary showing likeness (7)
23 A topic shifted line of sight (7)
24 A golf coach with new protective gear (5)

Down

1 Melodious musical composition grabbing little contralto (6)
2 Tottenham Hotspur claim debt notice is fake (8)
3 Food in bag rubbished (4)
4 Protected Greek character in ruined mine (6)
5 Cruise men modified when short of money and nervous (8)
6 Silver and argon jelly (4)
7 A director opening winter season (6)
13 Detective and quiet Queen bolt (8)
14 Important committee used for typing (8)
15 Dance around headless fish with clergyman (6)
17 Happily dallying about, not in (6)
18 Getting less wet laundry in garden? Not entirely (6)
20 Wanted naked wager (4)
22 A US city beginning to suffer sadly (4)

37

Across

1 Stop a break for the audience (6)
4 Feline make of car (6)
9 Portion of bread left out for dolt (3)
10 River with male and female warrior (9)
11 Understand attractive partner? (5)
12 West beset by working ambition? It's self-inflicted mistake (3,4)
14 Tirade in favour of the London Underground is sticking out (11)
17 Alien change of rule (7)
18 Leaves out award with sex appeal second (5)
20 European and American work digested as complicated (9)
22 Festival pass is returned (3)
23 Resist mad sibling (6)
24 Equilibrium in street unchanged (6)

Down

1 Immediately united about Cuba (2,4)
2 Concerning healthy makeover, perhaps (5)
3 Pasta cooked past eight? (9)
5 Wagon stripped earlier (3)
6 Horned beast in hackneyed material from college? (7)
7 King on northbound road concerns an organ (5)
8 One baby flag flying in part of Indian Ocean (3,2,6)
13 Pointer in home that's most restricted (9)
15 Engineering company dares to move studies again (7)
16 Assistants penning second secret comments (6)
17 Liberates fine Welsh male (5)
19 Aides revised plans (5)
21 Be in debt to some rowers (3)

38

Across

8 Stumble, permit three rhyming lines (7)
9 Game I play to make mental picture (5)
10 Frenzied attack engulfing Belgium (5)
11 Rioters possibly revel noisily (7)
12 Shortened form spread above Britain (12)
16 Untie yacht? It surprisingly supplies genuine feel (12)
20 Singer with mass intervening to show nervousness? (7)
23 Doorkeepers putting off hard consumers (5)
24 Turkish title in use once more (5)
25 Published policy in summary (7)

Down

1 Shop keep (5)
2 Mouthful by mouthful, losing points gradually (3,2,3)
3 Aircraft with good cover and key radius (6)
4 Agitate prison (4)
5 Car taken by graduate gets fewest points (6)
6 King prone to be enraptured (4)
7 Exhausting attention received in part of plane (7)
13 Large vessel in elevator (3)
14 Smash hit near – I find it's about to happen (2,3,3)
15 Caribbean native, a hit in a ground (7)
17 English books in front of grammarian in decline (6)
18 Enumerates Earls (6)
19 Key is permitted (5)
21 Cheese manufactured in retirement (4)
22 School's memo rising (4)

39

Across

7 Sound again concerning English singers, not Irish (2-4)
8 Rated woman due for transfer (6)
9 Superb time with king recalled (4)
10 Chance I had to get into style of speaking (8)
11 Race, say, in principle of the free market? (11)
14 Our stealing broke the rules (11)
18 Spin coin side to make choice (8)
19 Skilled element in tableware (4)
20 Take in fool, backward Australian creature (6)
21 A sign of faith in this type of clue? (6)

Down

1 Politician angrily orates without Nationalist (7)
2 One round hospital in persistent pain (4)
3 Racing vehicle track returns after move without constant speed (2-4)
4 Headless chaos with skinned yeti bird (6)
5 Happy garlic mayonnaise without hint of albumen or flowers (8)
6 Rules cited? They're in riders' hands (5)
12 Former priest with financial debts seen after parking (8)
13 Surround middle of tent with US actress (7)
15 Academic institution finishes off event before board showing togetherness (6)
16 Cancel adopting adult every year (6)
17 Bind the French tree (5)
19 Broadcasts arrogance (4)

Across

1 A guy is free from worry (2,4)
4 Ice-covered marsh holds royal fictional kingdom (6)
8 Cover in swimming pool, not old (3)
9 It's poison mixing opinions (9)
11 Noble was not late and not unknown (4)
12 Single time to enter award that's antiquated (8)
15 Curious ban on TV to gag very independent socialite (3,6)
18 Final opening in EU taken by a liberal (8)
19 Fear easily contained in region (4)
21 After rocky road, musical magazine finds National Trust decoration (9)
23 Trouble in sound of intoxicating drink (3)
24 Arouse former state (6)
25 Work given unusual need begun (6)

Down

1 Colleagues offering a liberal number of stories (6)
2 Corrected a blunder over English – like a minor pain? (9)
3 Drinks lightly and falls with litre drained (4)
5 Logical man after food portion (8)
6 Travel very quickly with minute gone in animal park (3)
7 Like a brooding bird and Russian dolls? (6)
10 Astatine splits majestic change from solid to gas (9)
13 Amuse and confuse entire ant (9)
14 Natural feeling in good man in court (8)
16 Busy figure round river is suited (6)
17 Pinned down trouble in revolutionary study (6)
20 Prevent pans ascending (4)
22 Senior citizen hides monster (3)

Across

1 Dry figure amid prosperous period showing staying power (6)
5 Put an end to whisky (6)
8 Heard to climb with an ache (4)
9 Passes over, say, lecturer between two Poles (8)
10 Wild sheep near Galilee in part (6)
11 Set had altered departures (6)
12 Rogue heard in main body of church (4)
14 Nothing found in Manila (3)
15 Duplicate specimen of book (4)
16 Pal seen at beginning of Saturday? (6)
18 A teaching graduate touring America gets insulted (6)
20 Sinister influence creating evil snag (8)
22 Elitist, old boy's after tin (4)
23 Acknowledges a daughter and son touring US college (6)
24 That woman's after no eats! (6)

Down

2 No grim smell (5)
3 Youthful agent working round middle of week (7)
4 Cited end with note I'm altering (9)
5 Decline in sales agreed (3)
6 Nothing very good in final letter (5)
7 Get up to date with strike at college (5,2)
11 Spotted dog upset boy at main ground (9)
13 A posh car in front of ramshackle dive gained recognition (7)
15 Difficult periods interrupted by upper-class pleasure trips (7)
17 Some unspoken nuisance – or boredom (5)
19 Eastern European after revolution to run away (5)
21 With pressure gone, ignore fool (3)

Across

1 Drains put back in resorts (4)
4 Versatile cyclist heading off to tour Turkey in regular fashion (8)
8 Spirit in shifty spy and revolutionary (6)
9 Former British thriller director, conquering figure (6)
10 Affectedly pretty woollen cloth clipped (4)
11 Shields detective in varied ports (8)
13 Change allegiance while dancing? (5,3,5)
16 Star's mood fluctuates without love in old Russian territories (8)
19 Analyse river (4)
20 Rustic and wealthy sort talk informally (6)
22 Rules in showers, we hear (6)
23 Footman in Belgium and Spain showing result of a blow? (5,3)
24 Name established for home (4)

Down

2 Predicament with promises for key to computing? (9)
3 Staff largely put in groups? They're kept under wraps (7)
4 State after crashing? (5)
5 Corrected about broken tower (7)
6 Boat, no external staff (5)
7 The French and English in the sheltered side (3)
12 Large numbers provide stuff on beach in south possibly (9)
14 Initially traded foreign currency producing bother (7)
15 Frolicking valiant Eastern European (7)
17 Spell in charge of old letters (5)
18 Work in the military and start court action? (5)
21 Valuable liquid starts to ooze into luggage (3)

Across

8 Clue misguided about northern relative (5)
9 First person, we're told, left on tree hair (7)
10 Test Warsaw resident, perhaps, lacking nothing for instance (7)
11 European, a radical, having attentive capability? (5)
12 One French tree surrounds yew, say, and isn't liked (9)
14 Dandies lose nothing in shoot-'em-up style of game (inits) (3)
15 Say further in a couple of days (3)
16 What's behind conflict over river storage area? (9)
19 US measure satisfied monarch (5)
21 Conductor West rots wildly (7)
23 Defective peacekeepers overlooking body of water (7)
24 Time, perhaps, in Yemen wasted (5)

Down

1 Office in old city kept by dandy (6)
2 Got rid of terrible cars US actor overturned (8)
3 Assist man with old record (4)
4 Cancel exercise in kingdom largely (6)
5 Academic work about outwardly strange curved structure (8)
6 Duo's soft tune (4)
7 Protection against sun – or colours? (6)
13 Mighty prisoner, fellow breaking new rule (8)
14 Figure from tour relaxing during fine poetic evening (8)
15 Big load to carry is dangerous, not hard (6)
17 I'm ready to go round without a cure (6)
18 Derived name in English horse with Frenchman (6)
20 Tense question in job (4)
22 Former Prime Minister's garden (4)

Across

1 Pick up unusual angle (5)
4 Assignment in religious institution (7)
9 Like a criminal set (8)
10 Opera song in bar I adored (4)
11 Start midday meal containing hint of avocado (6)
12 Criticize error in tennis (5)
13 Award enthrals old music maker (4)
15 Oddly loiter and don't tell the truth (3)
16 Kurd understanding somewhat Asian language (4)
17 Minister stripped of power for crime (5)
19 Bridge players beginning to receive award in dress (6)
21 Dash inside hotel anxiously (4)
22 Goes on two wheels again and serves a green cause? (8)
23 Keeps rates in ground (7)
24 Ground covered in shrub hard after sign of summer? (5)

Down

2 Large priest is an animal (5)
3 Capone almost injured firm (2,5)
5 At home, change produces lack of concern (12)
6 University supporters held up in total mess (inits) (5)
7 US college with time in dictionary left out (7)
8 After ages, hunting loner is crazy (2,3,4,3)
14 Type that's raised with difficulty entering Scottish bank (7)
16 A little bag? Rule it misguided when carrying first of cases (7)
18 Medical institution thanks deliverer of presents (5)
20 Grumble from 50 amid defeat (5)

45

Across

1 Goes for a levy, we hear (7)
5 Foreign decree misrepresenting sea east of Britain (5)
9 Cool oligarch after revolution concealing name according to time (13)
10 Grant pen to be replaced in the club? (8)
11 Lights left out showing measure of current (4)
12 Éclair cut wrongly for spread (9)
16 Risk driver's first encountered with wintry phenomenon (4)
17 iPhone installation drifts with permits (8)
19 Uncomplaining passenger's first on ship with alcohol I fancy (13)
21 Idly ramble round lake in picturesque place (5)
22 Quiet putting for gaming (7)

Down

2 Casual garment Trish sported close to court (1-5)
3 Adjacent aspect of a bulky building? (9)
4 Foreign currency raised in Amman or Kabul (5)
6 Knock out one carp (3)
7 Overwhelms Frenchman in exchanges (6)
8 Cruise company last at sea regarding mail (6)
11 Expert writer with sex appeal and unknown following (9)
13 Heard syllabus is rough (6)
14 Man occupying squalid digs sounded dejected (6)
15 Discharged marine to stay (6)
18 Young dog with the Italian student (5)
20 Behold large and humorous text (inits) (3)

Across

7 Graduate beginning to imbibe Asian cocktail (3,3)
8 Only Minnesota grave (6)
9 That lady deserted the hut (4)
10 Section covered in profanities! (8)
11 Exceptional exit position (11)
14 Messenger, maybe, with laugh about ransom with nothing taken (11)
18 Value highly honey (8)
19 Professor backs Pole and gives assent (4)
20 Draw internal musket chambers (6)
21 Film covering Welsh solicitor (6)

Down

1 Wife wrongly shut a book in bathing unit (7)
2 Boss in horse-breeding establishment (4)
3 Jamboree festival is fantastic without 5 or 50? (6)
4 Go up a small crater first, next to border (6)
5 Instrument deployed in cartel (8)
6 Change represented by noon? (5)
12 Menial types ending in lesser vehicle in groups (8)
13 Date teased about intent (4,3)
15 Hug not doctored for love (6)
16 Use a lot of milk sloppily as breakfast fare (6)
17 Smashed with no money (5)
19 Reports in four directions (4)

Across

1 Astonish with moving leg behind marsh (6)
5 Allies' enemy captures Order of Merit with principles (6)
8 Babble back a long story (4)
9 Expert details middle of weather outlook (8)
10 Cake, a couple of toasties – and ice cream (6)
11 Name largely Rex in charge of lemons etc (6)
12 A drink, middle of kebab, and jealousy – not new! (4)
14 Woman wore valuable coats (3)
15 Look in earl, say (4)
16 Iceland prosecutes problems (6)
18 Outcome pleasing to workforce? (3-3)
20 Crocheting with king holding fool and bone, possibly (8)
22 Strongly dislike speed with seconds gone (4)
23 Longs to see Norway during parts of decade (6)
24 Finale say about Northern racket (6)

Down

2 Old container close to fridge is egg-shaped (5)
3 Type of bread that sounds like an old folk's home? (7)
4 Lookers take in politican with cry of attention for users (9)
5 A very old monetary unit in Macau (3)
6 Type of some tin putty (5)
7 Computer manufactured in Cheam (7)
11 Bubbly companion with innovative game plan left out (9)
13 Meaning of part of the Bible removed from confusing sentences (7)
15 Gangnam Style singer on revolutionary day is excited (7)
17 Speak of golf club without power (5)
19 Be in harmony with motor racing element (3,2)
21 Idaho beginning to scrutinize official cards (abbr) (3)

48

Across

8 Stopped alternative to bread (7)
9 Radiate energy, 10 dudes stripped (5)
10 Crazy rage follows drug longing (5)
11 Almost halt fury with place for safekeeping (7)
12 Massage lip with pain, message isn't relevant (12)
16 King or client wrongly fitting together (12)
20 Rogue claimed for health check (7)
23 Norwegian king captured by search (5)
24 Aristocrat, one disturbed about British left (5)
25 Overloaded Slough editor (7)

Down

1 Located evil duke (5)
2 Daughter hung out possibly for fried cake (8)
3 Excite prison in rebellion (4,2)
4 Increases marketing campaign, we hear (4)
5 Like an idol, English, in reformed choir (6)
6 Some reject unappetising fish (4)
7 Frenchman married in an invigorated state? (7)
13 Behold none in toilet! (3)
14 Prohibit Turk dancing around piano and bust (8)
15 Arranging about 1000 for shooting (7)
17 Salad ingredient to rise very rapidly (6)
18 Knowledge excited any African national (6)
19 Top performers in English city, we hear (5)
21 Director misplacing bet has obligation (4)
22 Speech defect in pupil is problematic (4)

Across

1 Hovis stripped with mould to become egg-shaped (7)
5 Here there's much love initially for internet language (inits) (4)
9 On the way to tense, old hospital rooms (7)
10 Carried Jason, missing umpteenth top (5)
11 Beat bean? (5)
12 Indian bread in city stimulating one's appetite? (6)
14 Put to rest note scribbled by doctor (6)
16 English dirge played making one more irritable (6)
18 African politicians in change of set position (6)
19 Intimate easily losing head (5)
22 Doctrine going up and down (5)
23 Something weird in strange loch, perhaps (7)
24 Alternately corrects monsters (4)
25 Browsing town (7)

Down

2 I, perhaps, swear before the French return (5)
3 Make drink round men in plant (6-2-3)
4 Hurries from skirmishes with leader removed (6)
6 Designation in India for stations (7)
7 Ogle at crank with no middle (4)
8 Plain daughter took a pace (7)
10 Woman in New York tended to be liberal (5-6)
13 Most dull engineers certainly in sports car (7)
15 Huge sign of appreciation among element in charge (7)
17 Mean mood rising among leaders of diehard extremists (6)
20 Father gets in East and North a song of praise (5)
21 German engineer's essential oil (4)

Across

1 Arrive with a farm worker and have a fall? (4,1,7)
8 Brief moment with outermost times in dangerous groups? (5)
9 Dumplings good with no chic cooking (7)
10 Joey has time for foundation (4)
11 Place largely in Aldi's designed for management (8)
14 Look of German's first long weapon (6)
15 Walked round lake among first three? (6)
17 Exact short glasses whenever it's at first cloudy (8)
18 Water source in good condition (4)
20 Bewitch with fondness, not quietly (7)
22 Knight returns with greeting for Hindu sage (5)
23 Posh breeder men upset round start of month not recalled (12)

Down

1 Caterer sighs having to adjust retailer's aid? (4,8)
2 Cook altered warm voice (9)
3 Part of church is leaderless? Error! (4)
4 Win back say capital in Royal Navy (6)
5 Cue alternate play on time (8)
6 Key confines convicts to some extent (abbr) (3)
7 Herb by yard like a friend loitered (5-7)
12 One following Sunday courses planned round college (9)
13 Deed I linked to a vet that's involved in stir (8)
16 Benefit of furtive fluid, not loud (6)
19 Dull poet brought up (4)
21 Dupe commanding officer before noon (3)

51

Across

1 Set fire to church behind hill (5)
4 Fool's holding special coils (6)
10 Set about illegal motoring manoeuvre (9)
11 Reserve diamonds (3)
12 Element in athletic or gifted dog (5)
13 An egg I scrambled, getting older (6)
14 Adorable star relaxed taking time out in body of water (8,3)
18 With weapon, hog is excited and enthusiastic (4-2)
20 Outspoken, provoked central California (5)
23 French King has European country's initials (inits) (3)
24 Fools celebrate what judges do? (9)
25 Smoothly crushed gelato (6)
26 Film award in November's wake? (5)

Down

2 Weirder 500 included in rising repeat (5)
3 Type passing on complaint in aircraft (7)
5 Question wife given present (5)
6 Biology, for example, with 101 in seance without answer (7)
7 Most of fabric brought to court (4)
8 Stupid person caught in hill of sand (5)
9 A series of cunning manoeuvres with Tom and Jerry (3,3,5)
15 Advanced thinking is humorous (7)
16 Welshman occupied by six subjects primarily studies for an exam (7)
17 Put straight evil male on way out (5)
19 Private worker is huge (5)
21 Some machinations in Eastern country (5)
22 Old artist with learner in exam? (4)

Across

8 Something to sit on right behind tea (5)
9 Attacks Indiana, Virginia, Delaware and Illinois finally (7)
10 Giants found in piccolo's sinfonietta (7)
11 Greek character in river's opening (5)
12 I'd warned possibly about a characteristic of the post-Victorian period? (9)
14 Some problem surprisingly in printing units (3)
15 Disruptive adolescent in revolutionary study (3)
16 Pressure on journalist probing not long ago earlier legal ruling (9)
19 Passion in park official right away (5)
21 Be upset by most of kiosk for glass (7)
23 Booming actor bringing happiness (7)
24 A university academic clutching right dress (5)

Down

1 It's pointedly frozen in one loop without radius (6)
2 Sanctified part of college due to receive money? (8)
3 Key part for viewing flower? (4)
4 Most of sport on island seen in scantily cut garment (6)
5 Reveal proof? (8)
6 One puppet, almost a hero (4)
7 Academic works for example on board Eastern ship (6)
13 Without first chapter, preacher's confused, so say it differently (8)
14 Vote neither returning particle (8)
15 Possibly, Barney is close (6)
17 Put in cipher enclosure with poem (6)
18 Skill embodied by monumental entertainer (6)
20 Attempts changes to a new system (4)
22 Student group invested in Skye art (4)

Across

1 Mountain service provided (6)
5 Summon damned drunk (6)
8 A fine Arab in the distance (4)
9 Pry by rough pub and plunge quickly (8)
10 Disadvantage with odd fleet – it returns with small scraps of paper! (8)
11 Lounge revealing a lot of money (4)
12 Source of sound expertise initially in exotic store (6)
14 Good phrase endlessly contrived in plots (6)
16 Employs tricks right away (4)
18 Sweater I damaged in a kind of way (2,2,4)
20 Sub, maybe, in Kent town (8)
21 No part for short death notice (4)
22 Spirit welcome in Western broadcaster (6)
23 Great fears about to be admitted by fathers (6)

Down

2 A loud façade is an insult (7)
3 Son with enthusiasm held up a type? (5)
4 Party Italy devised showing purpose (13)
5 Set apart and quivering, hide in disgust (13)
6 Setter, uninteresting, with ace bone marrow (7)
7 Verse found in Christmas book (5)
13 Lives with team in reserve (7)
15 Hastened ride moving under hot old city (7)
17 Cut line in band (5)
19 Utter what's at back of hollow predicament (5)

Across

7 Advocate mixing of clues? No! (7)
9 Lover of pop beginning to make a lot of capital (5)
10 Long period in private only (3)
11 Places where titles are borrowed? (9)
12 Exceptionally good type of policeman (5)
14 French article present in kitchen's confines – or not ascertained? (7)
16 Fall asleep? It could produce prod (4,3)
18 Objects to it on typography measures (5)
19 Finished a wall while drunk? (9)
20 Submachine gun gripped by Suzie (3)
21 Claw embedded in Catalonia (5)
22 Seeks to explain pardons (7)

Down

1 Expert document principally about old tax is retrieved (8)
2 Mention of aquatic bird in circular motion (4)
3 Some jostle regularly stable worker? (6)
4 English doctor with chest to board ship (6)
5 Drunken Romeo swallowed revolting French wine, he'll eat anything (8)
6 Damages planet (4)
8 Delivery follows this violence in workers (6,5)
13 It is likely for beauty to eat head of lettuce (8)
15 Cattiness mixed without cocaine is the worst (8)
17 Choosing work with the sound of a small bell (6)
18 Prevail upon popular French aristocrat with energy (6)
19 Sinks vessels (4)
20 Former state in America with southern river (inits) (4)

Across

7 Politician entering republic, large dominion (6)
8 Intervene with note amid manipulation of news (4,2)
9 Children promote son and lose grip (4)
10 Everything assumed in discussion of college poetry? (8)
11 Unusual cat farm's own female engaged in basketry say (11)
14 Induct gnome randomly logging (11)
18 Degrees climb without a loud musical symbol (4,4)
19 See trendy cut of meat (4)
20 Become preoccupied with mad bosses (6)
21 Remember to phone again (6)

Down

1 They cure people who puff? (7)
2 Compel to throw away diamonds (4)
3 Removes listening devices in upcoming plot Gus designed (6)
4 Mike's fantastic love for arctic resident (6)
5 Material about the old eastern Mediterranean (8)
6 Wash off part of mandarin seed (5)
12 Pace of paw of cats and dogs returning (8)
13 Dub tile cracked beneath hospital department (7)
15 Except if sun lessens partly (6)
16 Exertion encapsulated by chef for tourists (6)
17 Exotic set of steps taken in by Swiss ambassador (5)
19 Location excluded opening cord (4)

Across

1 Take away Princess of Wales's weapon? (6)
4 Applies overcoat, perhaps, in past changes (6)
8 Marketing potential is partly suspicious (inits) (3)
9 One who erases writing and explains? (9)
11 Returning, come face to face with swarm (4)
12 Hear about a verse on establishment in parody (8)
15 Darwin, perhaps, ruined oil bigots (9)
18 Peer brandishing ties as most advanced (8)
19 Powder found in metal case (4)
21 Model expert has to enter data, perhaps (9)
23 Company that sells broadband is soft (inits) (3)
24 Special stroke makes a mark (6)
25 Views parts of play (6)

Down

1 Note crooked stub producing suspicions (6)
2 Odd step taken by male cutting beer brewed in month (9)
3 Liverpool players hired special housing (4)
5 Nice cheers? (2,6)
6 Pen tip made of nickel and boron (3)
7 Sprinkles small soft sea creatures (6)
10 Start to see your lies possibly in grave fashion (9)
13 Spot mostly oak unit? It's poorly made (9)
14 Cloaks game (8)
16 Entices agency worker with this emptied (6)
17 Son deals with ranges (6)
20 Soldier that's hired car? (4)
22 Bird howls at heart (3)

Across

1 Understands four points (4)
4 Fighter altering trade went abroad (8)
8 Exemplified Mum's scrawled pair of notes (6)
9 Ridiculous metal chip (6)
10 Left impression in secluded place (4)
11 Look after moving animation without love (8)
13 Polite English name in Eire resettled, a builder of bridges? (5,8)
16 Demanded unusual tidiness (8)
19 Former volunteers twice getting farewell (2-2)
20 Earn a container – holding thanks! (6)
22 Hit, or don't, in baseball (6)
23 Infiltrates air conditioning with 100 letters, perhaps (8)
24 Mention Eastern Europeans getting permits (4)

Down

2 Count idea wrong in schooling (9)
3 Drunk Asia rum for warrior (7)
4 Frenchman devised demo for computer device (5)
5 Steering corporation without liberal among Government (7)
6 Take over a party with point (5)
7 Twelve-point measurement unit in remission (inits) (3)
12 I damage current equipment used to produce criminals' likenesses (9)
14 Formerly looks after and develops (7)
15 Unsophisticated and not sharp (7)
17 Cross part of choir at Easter (5)
18 Daughter sits not quietly getting quantities of medicine (5)
21 Credit almost instinctive reaction (3)

Across

1 Fashions overdose in drugs (7)
5 Increased bit of work? Measure of work recalled (4)
9 Take for granted page on CV (7)
10 Condemn cowhide crypt covering (5)
11 Name of a book competition (5)
12 Hostility from men confused by one hollow toy (6)
14 Unqualified nurse takes strain (6)
16 Apprehensive group of countries when in European yard (6)
18 Period trailing river, source of photos? (6)
19 Partly contemporary speed (5)
22 China/Estonia bureau (5)
23 Plant I moved before start of year not in fitting manner (7)
24 Ornamental stone in Northern yard in old times (4)
25 Tree lad transplanted and changed (7)

Down

2 Some able lecturers return (5)
3 Sourest hare struggled with confinement (5,6)
4 Thought with first person in action (6)
6 Cheese I cart to eccentric (7)
7 Roads move side to side, front to back (4)
8 Saw quiffed man behind place (7)
10 Prove matter's done wrongly (11)
13 Son brought up New York internally on my return, which means the same (7)
15 Hear about old type of drama (7)
17 A group of spies in opposing directions regarding stock (6)
20 Dull element in team attending (5)
21 Reflection of sound in English choir, not Irish (4)

Across

1 Transmission reaching climax after Sunday (7)
5 Fish stick (4)
10 Helps idiot with tables left out (7)
11 Atmospheres artist found in Australia (5)
12 Flower in place set up around lake on island (5)
13 Idle talk bachelor ignored in agitated state (6)
15 Prayer's old, jail lacks leader (6)
17 Robber, say, in southern Poland for stint (6)
19 Last word with daughter and son making changes (6)
20 Girl has no rope (5)
23 Free relative without starter (5)
24 Instrument has nothing on barbed weapon (7)
25 Discover part of Sussex (4)
26 Cooking in gravy subject to change (7)

Down

2 Support for artist in picture, a selfie (5)
3 Inspector's put in post and let down (12)
4 Curl up in den with the French (6)
6 Middle Eastern citizen, former PM taking day off (7)
7 Golfer with energy instead (4)
8 Sequence in a comic drawing by artist (7)
9 Notably father disfigured liar curtly (12)
14 Fix a quiet conclusion (7)
16 Prisoners put lidless rubbish container on friends (7)
18 Hat Sam moved getting breathing difficulties (6)
21 Hospital in broadcast is revealed (5)
22 Temporary dwellings closed, first to last (4)

Across

7 Currency left twice in winding road (6)
8 Connected with operating queue (6)
9 A fool appears very quickly (inits) (4)
10 Discourage covering cot around scanner, perhaps (8)
11 Bard's odes analysed with approval – source of geographical information? (7,4)
14 Exciting ancient language? It's mug possibly embracing it (11)
18 It's pride that could make one lively (8)
19 Picks work on northbound street (4)
20 Unknown editor wearing, returning unfashionable dinner jacket (6)
21 Smouldering remains in December spectacle (6)

Down

1 Leading team making cut (7)
2 Turn over female component of face (4)
3 Swaps careers (6)
4 Without jittery Noel, strange buttonhole creates Jacuzzi (3,3)
5 Erase and faint (8)
6 Marriage in university west of Ontario (5)
12 Came back elected? (8)
13 Where one's located before delivery? (2,5)
15 Came across backward note in system (6)
16 Los Angeles succumbs to women (6)
17 Narcotic's the best without hint of tranquilizer or medication (5)
19 Circles absorb show partly (4)

Across

1 Do sit correctly for verse writer (5)
4 Saint and first sinner rises (6)
10 Rigged vegan data for a head start (9)
11 Bananas and nuts! (3)
12 Handwriting expert embraces suggestion (5)
13 With leader gone, dreads slips (6)
14 Bus kept cash disguised to transfer responsibility (4,3,4)
18 Obtained auricle reflecting study (6)
20 Cuts off the top of barley and wheat? (5)
23 Some or lots short of money (3)
24 Matter-of-fact fool in charge blocked by meeting (9)
25 Steal coat (6)
26 Take over illegally much of lending practice with power (5)

Down

2 Inspector has vehicle and sofa (5)
3 Second reigns possibly for musical performers (7)
5 Traders originally? One succeeds belonging to them (5)
6 Almost without feeling, Queen 99 involves digits (7)
7 Foam potatoes without pea, say (4)
8 Expression of irritation about new bombastic declarations (5)
9 Make a lot of noise in vigil with the deceased (4,3,4)
15 Examine bank-less canals? Excitingly, yes! (7)
16 Suits in British city? Some require tailoring (7)
17 Prepare southern young Conservative in pub (5)
19 Even parts of ones epic act for charity (inits) (5)
21 Striking royal exterior (5)
22 Part of leg in young cow (4)

62

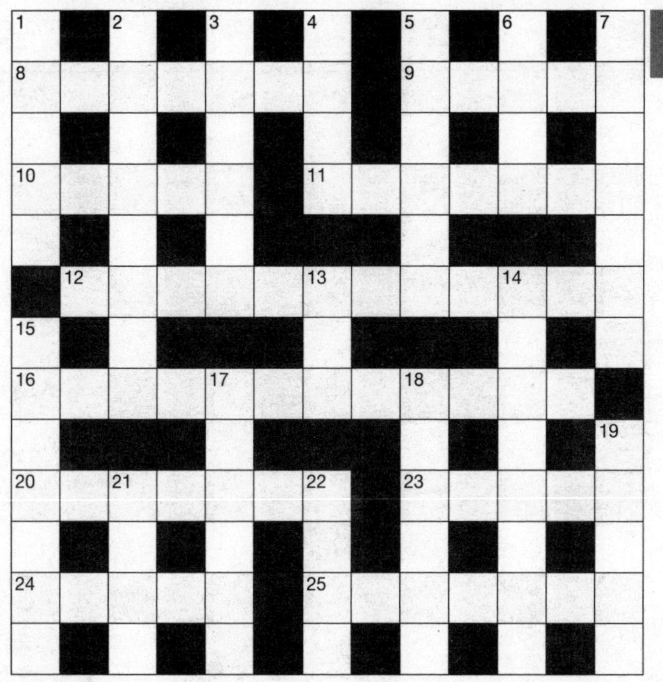

Across

8 Country alcoholics group accepts mixed crime (7)
9 Suspended like skating? (2,3)
10 Screen, we hear, Eastern European (5)
11 Wrongly take single woman present, it's said (7)
12 Verify gold, then twitch and swirl tea (12)
16 Evict Presley tumbling in the order given (12)
20 Say chocolate bar quietly? (7)
23 Extremes of seaside alcoholic drink makes a cure! (5)
24 Two foreign articles falling short (5)
25 Esteeming insurer's work? (7)

Down

1 Equal game (5)
2 Regrets about uniform incomes (8)
3 In weight, hefty – like last one in a rowing boat? (6)
4 Salve produced by half of Scottish castle (4)
5 Bosnia cultivated dwarf tree (6)
6 Annoy king on French island (4)
7 Bar deed that's out of order like an imam, say (7)
13 Part of tennis in one tournament (3)
14 Sensitive to every bit of work at just above freezing (8)
15 Adult with note in band (5-2)
17 Exporter with anger producing lapse (6)
18 Victor left in a place that's dirty hugely (6)
19 I work after morning for foreign friend (5)
21 Digital phone protocol is Dutch and new (inits) (4)
22 Ramble in wood heading off (4)

63

Across

1 Silo built for petroleum products (4)
4 Naughty Gore produces angry feeling (3,5)
8 Stunted cigarette, end times! (6)
9 Ape thin Scotsman shedding pounds (6)
10 Actual regret after time (4)
11 Delight in legal defence? Certainly (8)
13 Big company works to annual limit (13)
16 Spilled in salt at sunken city (8)
19 Allotment's soft area used for filming (4)
20 All-points bulletin, about 50 syllable, for self-assurance (6)
22 Muscles press up in descent from height (6)
23 One making pronouncement on small electroacoustic devices (8)
24 Games company in periods in recession (4)

Down

2 Break trip tuner devised (9)
3 Inflict topic on citizen (7)
4 Purchase the whole stock of British university? Certainly! (3,2)
5 Fool, maybe, having hair turned back? (7)
6 Puts up regardless with swellings (5)
7 Virginia is after duck eggs (3)
12 Son in gear surprisingly that shows some logic (9)
14 Conspicuous problem in busy restaurant? (7)
15 Is against work with models (7)
17 A capital almost linked to a stench (5)
18 Badges for celebrities (5)
21 Narrowly defeat seed (3)

Across

7 Woman carrying holy books or sexy material (7)
9 Old judge to give a speech (5)
10 Kit with no good organ (3)
11 Quick trains in states (9)
12 Headless Jeremy confused mineral (5)
14 Overlooks Italian gentleman, first to last (7)
16 Dim male getting puzzled creates quandary (7)
18 Month associated with German saying (5)
19 Red sail? Cost I worked with (9)
20 Scheduled a group (3)
21 Money at home pocketed by Greek character (5)
22 Mostly unnecessary sewing items (7)

Down

1 Minister always to stop behind rector (8)
2 Row under black pig (4)
3 Strong wines cultivated beside yard (6)
4 Rule right to be observed in good cooker (6)
5 Language without rebel leader stuffing gear (8)
6 Asks for charity say in the Bahamas (4)
8 Close thought shown in seeking of work? (11)
13 Diverse and stimulating, without rector and without Catholic! (8)
15 Sturgeon, perhaps, regulated this cost (8)
17 Dame cultivated old western grassland (6)
18 Substance of significance (6)
19 Withered, partly crease-resistant (4)
20 Special dwarf personality (4)

Across

1 Raw fear that's spread in armed conflict (7)
5 Prejudice I detected among graduates (4)
9 Application in favour of weight (7)
10 Stacks jumbled without 100 chores (5)
11 Lecturer consumed by money in fight (5)
12 Last stout drunk captivating Frenchman (6)
14 Joining of particle after most of trouble (6)
16 Visage is handsome, partly, for Japanese entertainer (6)
18 Stoat hidden in copper mine (6)
19 Join with a loud scam (5)
22 Article extended throughout (5)
23 Pairs overthrow the French (7)
24 Daughter certainly in colours (4)
25 Perhaps, one regent I upset (7)

Down

2 Pythagoras partly used to visit here? (5)
3 River company with minute source of gain about to appear (11)
4 Gossip bringing drink on outing first off (6)
6 Firmly maintains varied sit-ins close to campus (7)
7 Tolerable pair of musical notes (2-2)
8 Mark out enigmatic spy chief leaving hospital (7)
10 A true eccentric going after moderate heat (11)
13 Spoil 10 contents of lists for someone on the left (7)
15 Miser's self-importance and creatures return (7)
17 Serve in prison, perhaps, as a shining light (6)
20 Artificial fellow spilt ales (5)
21 Set down large support (4)

66

Across

1 A cut devised on a line is concrete (6)
4 Distinction in cricket side within period of time (6)
9 Remain without a pen (3)
10 Single art playing percussion instruments (9)
11 Movable festival's not small for diner (5)
12 Get on with the French soprano forever young (7)
14 Gingerly note vanity let to spread (11)
17 One forcing his way into jetty by church, right? (7)
18 Fish to slide smoothly? (5)
20 Awkward gap in guide lacking bit of data, subject of test? (6,3)
22 Dread part of seaweed (3)
23 Enlist emblem in court (4,2)
24 Evaluate donkeys by first sanctuary (6)

Down

1 Response Americans were harbouring (6)
2 Have a stab at Saint for affair (5)
3 Six-footer, a Catholic with nervous habit, in polar region (9)
5 Have within – know now! (3)
6 Feline almost rising with fine place to find petroleum (3,4)
7 South-eastern lord ascends? (5)
8 This man possibly before work in railway shows hatred of men (11)
13 Contemplates vines cultivated over eons (9)
15 Late part of day becoming more level? (7)
16 Assigns official royal stamp principally (6)
17 Gapes about with footmen (5)
19 Rouse a King amid fear (5)
21 Old coin pocketed by executive (3)

67

Across

6 Attractive female that is supporting economy (5)
7 Like a normal narrative, say, in real novel (6)
9 General protective garment (7)
10 Shellfish unprepared in Portugal and Norway (5)
11 Some earth and a form of water (4)
13 Set towards east or north in arranged tie (6)
15 Worth in footman largely around university (5)
16 Decide in advance, or day after initially trendy (6)
17 Mock Jack with English queen (4)
20 Sir Francis found hiding in reeds, perhaps (5)
22 Becomes aware of section to be rewritten (7)
23 Select part of train noise at 135 degrees (6)
24 Male singer entertaining independent foundation (5)

Down

1 Looked after, detonated, exploded missing wheel (8)
2 Part of a flower, soft with the others (5)
3 Soprano taken with lady's jacket repeatedly in secretive fashion (5)
4 Animate popular father holding power (7)
5 Figures, maybe, found in band at arena (4)
6 Angry Greek island, we hear, in point for critical decision (10)
8 Fool with belief in America in investment institutions (4,6)
12 Dashed off right article (3)
13 Ordinary universal time absent (3)
14 Trouble in written school task (8)
15 Colonial ruler with defect runs over yard (7)
18 Headless victor is close to the centre (5)
19 Disorganized boss holding tons as Scottish stakes (5)
21 Dipsomaniac hydrates partly in pain (4)

68

Across

8 Stray mule worried rival (7)
9 Sound car by circle (5)
10 Constant note with unknown rice (5)
11 Wager in action held up? (7)
12 Corrupt clan led a city by chance (12)
16 Tome composed over year sound about derivations? (12)
20 Christmas poem by daughter given meaning? (7)
23 Unscripted commercial bile recalled without point (2-3)
24 One barely appearing to accept good reminder (5)
25 Offspring grasps incline with type of cheese (7)

Down

1 That man records with aids (5)
2 Tavern with brief lice liability outlined by the state (8)
3 Baku excited knight with one form of Japanese drama (6)
4 Tear apart some children decisively (4)
5 Direct a male that's raised croquet stick (6)
6 Some maid lying in unproductive fashion (4)
7 Benefit with extra farewell (7)
13 Building blocks don't begin to make self-confidence (3)
14 Small tree parts make brochures (8)
15 Advancing in league finale (7)
17 Lots of topless pasta! (6)
18 Sloping typeface from European country? (6)
19 Steak with infectious disease atop European (1-4)
21 Fake English in cryptic form of communication (4)
22 Attractive person gets something to eat in restaurant (4)

69

Across

1 Popular clothing material? A lot is found under bed (6)
5 Prohibit an acre for fruit (6)
8 Some see crumbling fawn (4)
9 Care of tenor possibly when holding note in musical composition (8)
10 Sign in British thriller writer (6)
11 Shrewdness in comedian of old (6)
12 Crossing in the direction of Germany (4)
14 Weapon in shooting undiscovered (3)
15 Junction done differently (4)
16 Excellent trophy for all to see recalled in ideal place (6)
18 Two journalists have it corrected (6)
20 Dandy penguin? (8)
22 I make an offer in the same place (4)
23 Group support's couch (6)
24 Piece of cloth is lifted about front of this elevated room (6)

Down

2 Old copper in credit to be found (5)
3 Came into contact with bloke with expression of pain inside (7)
4 Possibly a caring unionist is supported by a foreign country (9)
5 Dispose of wine container (3)
6 Works in bakery, we hear, for necessities (5)
7 Unathletic figure acquiring time with firm tennis shot (3,4)
11 US soul singer getting popular, source of great astonishment (9)
13 Anger at power cut covering penultimate suburb (7)
15 Having a greater volume? (7)
17 Gasp for breath, going round large factory (5)
19 One banished in former French island (5)
21 Mineral in minor exhibition (3)

70

Across

1 Avoid facing woman's garment (5)
4 Varied notes around bottom of till removed illegally (6)
10 Silly feet misplaced in a way of behaviour? (9)
11 French tea article (3)
12 A helper backing woman (5)
13 Drumming is rubbish also (6)
14 Trip captain devised for one in game? (11)
18 Confused Major with imaginary quantity and Japanese alphabet (6)
20 Some hope raising staged musical work (5)
23 Greek letter of interest when inflating tyres? (3)
24 Hate trade that's upset mortality level (5,4)
25 Vegetable found with speed? It's gone off! (6)
26 Coral island swaps wheel for tip of axle, in any way (2,3)

Down

2 Hidden back in cloak, fake Czech author (5)
3 Others with skill beginning again (7)
5 Tear around time for reward (5)
6 Lower gently – what a disappointment! (3,4)
7 Rejections from disheartened messages (4)
8 Wished, with liberal inside, for an edge (5)
9 Scan tacitly works regarding grammatical structure (11)
15 In this way spies in Alabama become hostile to others? (7)
16 One who can foresee gain by the sound of it (7)
17 Elite troops having iron in metal boxes (5)
19 Tree is more exposed having front missing (5)
21 Method of communication found in backwards Parliament (5)
22 Odyssey, perhaps, shown in fine pictures (4)

Across

7 Improve area in grip of revolutionary politician (6)
8 Select ring in elegant emerald at first (6)
9 Voice that's about lowest two octaves, for starters (4)
10 Barber company joins one very loud EU referendum leader (8)
11 A cold crying changed as a result (11)
14 Volume temporarily at home? (7,4)
18 Promotes round Northern Ireland disciplines? (8)
19 Greek character by church a great deal (4)
20 A start arranged for layers (6)
21 Len arranged superb cover with network? (6)

Down

1 Model businessman in charge in US city (7)
2 Thin pancake produced by a firm after time (4)
3 Made room between resort and church close to field (6)
4 Begin battle (6)
5 Flog back and hit one iron, perhaps (4,4)
6 I caught American in stress (5)
12 Author's fifth girl in a tawdry novel (8)
13 Devise pair of firms around Northern court (7)
15 Warm leftovers theatre cooked without starter (6)
16 Moved fast to see rugby outbuilding (6)
17 How one might find almost exactly filthy place? (5)
19 Rising religion rejecting society in African country (4)

Across

1 Teaching qualification needs parental guidance by state institution (inits) (4)
4 Faculty certainly in rowers? (8)
8 Lacquer without resin at first and disappear (6)
9 Former Anglican journalist in cap (6)
10 Aide revised plan (4)
11 Outlines of Indian city in indistinct sun (8)
13 Definitive writer with appeal backed musical (13)
16 Solid figure making lyric end (8)
19 Part of flock wanders nothing less (4)
20 Second creep produces untidy writing (6)
22 Straightens mixed signal (6)
23 Show team off rather (8)
24 Most of dog's outer coating (4)

Down

2 Those who judge pianos, perhaps (5,4)
3 Inscription – what's seen round mine apparently? (7)
4 Idiot rises around Henry's Jewish garment (5)
5 Stylish Eastern tangle muddled (7)
6 Suffer sudden attacks (not half) (5)
7 Heard expression of triumph with gardening tool (3)
12 Manoeuvres in political groupings (9)
14 Unfortunate hold-up after river for delivery animal? (7)
15 UK shirt manufactured, coming from Ankara? (7)
17 Foolish grandmother that is around (5)
18 Mix oats with hint of rye and grill (5)
21 Space out holding businessman (inits) (3)

73

Across

1 A prison in agitated state (5)
4 For each offence, surround a cat, perhaps (7)
9 Privately screen version during *X Factor* (2,6)
10 It's helpful for viewing French city (4)
11 Wound caused by rising painting on university mother (6)
12 A bishop always in imposing order (5)
13 Peter Pan character to appear with end coming earlier (4)
15 Torpedo boat area not yet disclosed (inits) (3)
16 Chances of winning are not even? (4)
17 Lowest point in Northern raid that's botched (5)
19 Information held by a Cyprus bureau (6)
21 It's used for baking loaves initially in family (4)
22 Multinational organization with open land is rare (8)
23 Bridge hidden in some chaos (7)
24 Recalled search bagging new joints (5)

Down

2 Arenas after area is cleared disseminated more sound (5)
3 Die of cold? (3,4)
5 Dug up an exact grave for outrageousness (12)
6 Note tailless bird characterized by natural energy? (5)
7 Teased woman, grandchild and daughter (7)
8 Rest connected as solution of a problem (12)
14 Refer to fellows into dancing (7)
16 Supply too many staff to accomplished king? (7)
18 Some food in error in restaurant (5)
20 Selected thing in Paris (5)

Across

1 A King round the bend with a fleet (6)
5 Flavours from free states (6)
8 Tourist attraction rings immediately (4)
9 Conservative individual defending dodgy unit to carry on (8)
10 Japanese island varying nosh in centre mostly (6)
11 Blows strongly around eastern visitors (6)
12 Spaceships feared objects principally in America (4)
14 Pair additionally cited (3)
15 Drums feature in such near soloists in part (4)
16 Twisted battle on foot (6)
18 Emitted light from lodge built round winter (6)
20 Send to sea after getting drunk with port (8)
22 Five kill for immorality (4)
23 Decreased right off and drew out (6)
24 Mess around with violin (6)

Down

2 Some mediocre trombonist recreating the past (5)
3 It's star that's disturbed creative types? (7)
4 Aristocrat entering outstanding department is valued (9)
5 Figure in haste negotiated (3)
6 Catch sixteen in Paris (5)
7 A quote disturbed Republican, producing dividing line (7)
11 Dismayed expression in dog I forget sadly lacking time (4,5)
13 Briefly showed US agent gripping part of whip (7)
15 Developed and turned headless (7)
17 Alarm put in shop, a nicety (5)
19 Better symbol for forty, we hear (5)
21 Concealed most of animal's skin (3)

75

Across

1 Passing quietly line hidden by short track (7)
5 Speechless nitwit lacking love (4)
9 A posh car sets out and stops (7)
10 Build eastern rectory (5)
11 Sudden wind has no oomph (5)
12 Inconvenienced, swapping parts for production (6)
14 Losing 1000 mounted warriors in periods of darkness (6)
16 Keep occupied English politician left over year (6)
18 Held sway, we hear, and was not dry? (6)
19 Tragic queen largely cherished by writer (5)
22 Similar source of knowledge in a story (5)
23 Belgian requiring translation for Indic language (7)
24 Sharp cry certainly overwhelming lecturer (4)
25 Decreases seminars, we hear (7)

Down

2 Reportedly, praises peers (5)
3 Stop seduction in ground (11)
4 Microorganism in no short supply (6)
6 Not uniform a French queen starts to advocate liberally (7)
7 Fliers for clubs (4)
8 Called about spirit showing fluctuation (7)
10 Bent moments, improper burials (11)
13 Burning material restricted in the middle of Egyptian monument (7)
15 Distant French lake, one taken in by female (7)
17 Take the gist from digestible mix that's safe to eat (6)
20 Doctor, with an instrument initially stuck in, to remove fluid (5)
21 Chap getting yen? Lots (4)

Across

1 Lawsuit about four? That's easy! (7)
5 Moles in small tarts (5)
9 Dodgy behaviour in comedian's act? (5,8)
10 Get maybe new storage unit (8)
11 Assistant parking on time (4)
12 Saw fake news – it's by press man (9)
16 Squad drink before motorway (4)
17 Expression in a large airport building (8)
19 Cartwheel, madly in love? (4,4,5)
21 Fast set of ships? (5)
22 Priest reviewed years for church ritual? (7)

Down

2 Rule publicly disclosed and overcome (6)
3 Slav in mad rampages producing wanton damage (9)
4 Baby misbehaving around English church (5)
6 Largely insignificant piece of verbal wit (3)
7 Spain and Norway getting token flag (6)
8 Idiot seizing established items of property (6)
11 Cathedral city follows summary to the letter (9)
13 Natural inhabitant is innocent, drinking tea, we hear (6)
14 Wheat for example put in a row, we hear (6)
15 Trouble in kind largely gets rating, say (6)
18 Uplifting period in posh car less common (5)
20 Finish in colour, we hear (3)

Across

1 I, perhaps, have second half of period in ecstasy (6)
4 Some question, one way or another (6)
8 Call for help from children not new (3)
9 What's left when answer is in memory jogger (9)
11 Hats like THIS? (4)
12 A music-maker with a tiny amount of money is nearby (8)
15 Formerly not working here in France with circle, by virtue of one's position (2,7)
18 Shocking choir awkwardly found round tree on way back (8)
19 Pursue barbarian tribe's leader (4)
21 Lost again, wistfully with sentimental longing (9)
23 Girl at home with article (3)
24 Confess editor's burned (6)
25 Many cooks including alternative sauce (6)

Down

1 Bug belonging to cult? (6)
2 Priest in organized parade is to vanish (9)
3 Ordinary guy (4)
5 Tiresome type is put in shade (8)
6 Used to own and hoard, oddly (3)
7 Kindness in month after conflict (6)
10 Nothing in gym I find altered – it's making partial changes? (9)
13 Gradual development of headless uprising (9)
14 Induce friend to carry religious books – four from Rome (8)
16 Quiet Spanish woman flourishes (6)
17 Dates arranged over year for girlfriend (6)
20 Month over in Irish county (4)
22 Source of heat's fallen slowly almost (3)

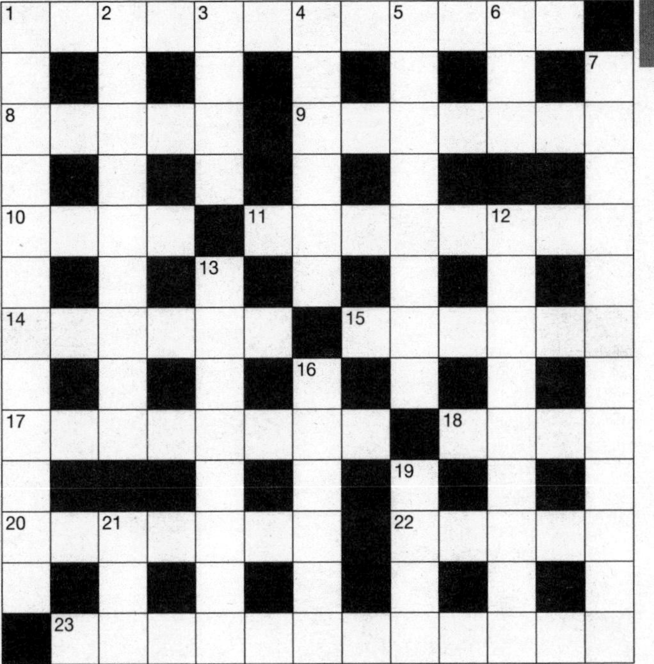

Across

1 Mathematical constants working well in Greek island (12)
8 Down under, I maybe make gas (5)
9 Girl holds number for receiver (7)
10 Ascertain refusal reportedly (4)
11 Disdain of prisoner with lure (8)
14 A tender European soprano remains (6)
15 Part of some trick characterising poetry? (6)
17 Some curt eccentric, one making purchase in store (8)
18 Wheeze from petrol pump, at first (4)
20 Copper, perhaps, with chaps in English service (7)
22 Repeated rejections raised about one bulb (5)
23 Key service producing minimum of resources (8,4)

Down

1 Unmotivated worker gets to strike guard? (5-7)
2 Incomes analysed round firm in academic study (9)
3 Loud colour that's a good accompaniment to Ginger? (4)
4 Prisoner captured beam of light with drawing utensil (6)
5 Earl has northern bird escorted and christened (8)
6 Yellowish-brown cistern mostly (3)
7 Separate 99 independent rubbish competitors (12)
12 Caribbean island cocktail (9)
13 Radical scribbled note about left that's suggestive (8)
16 Football team I let stupidly into cricket club (6)
19 Indian island with liberal objective (4)
21 Stray in section of territory (3)

79

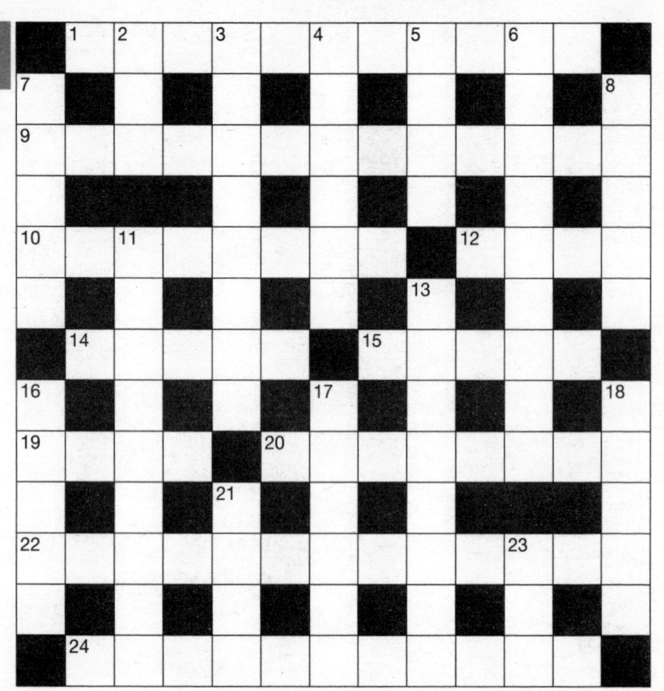

Across

1 Like outer areas of a city concerned with US leader losing power? (11)
9 Briefly, deal is rare (2,5,6)
10 Allowing new linen bag (8)
12 Disgusting civil engineer housing (4)
14 Sex appeal shown by woman in steamy place? (5)
15 Special equipment for young person (5)
19 Skipper with male in part of house (4)
20 Dependant sporting orange in confines of haven (6-2)
22 Sportsman with sister and agents into stylized speaking (13)
24 Founder hires tables that are rickety (11)

Down

2 Greek god devoid of right? No, Greek goddess (3)
3 Club threw out with fellow missing medical apparatus (4,4)
4 Having a meal in chairs devoid of sun (6)
5 So overwhelmed by enthusiasm (4)
6 I rifle about under a politician for equipment to increase volume (9)
7 Named and seen reportedly (5)
8 Produced with keyboard some arty pedagogy (5)
11 Kindred disturbed a US lagoon (9)
13 See schooner, say, showing tiny telescope (8)
16 Drawing talk in good hotel (5)
17 Discontinue clean reforms round college (6)
18 Single Northern director in an upright position (2,3)
21 Neighbour put back brass instrument (4)
23 Walk not hard for ex-US president (3)

Across

1 By the way, my last half of chickens can read minds (7)
5 Sits in the sun with head covered and poses (4)
9 Deeply emotional way to describe how verbs can differ? (7)
10 Looks for special smells without recipe (5)
11 I wander back for Polynesian figure (5)
12 Take no notice of some sign or event (6)
14 Parts of guns and spectacles (6)
16 Harmonious pattern starts to reinforce happiness? Distorted myth (6)
18 Weights showing colour on board (6)
19 Flanks in teams (5)
22 Lew settled in New York recently (5)
23 Peculiar trade followed by Republican in backward period (7)
24 Declares yen to be among elite soldiers (4)
25 Take back engineers with motoring group in motor sports event (7)

Down

2 Some tennis additionally, we hear, producing argument (3-2)
3 Level of performance as thickness? (11)
4 Anger, nearly steal in the spirit of peace (6)
6 Seen confused sailor rise and mock (5,2)
7 Band in concerts as heralded (4)
8 Fire is close to firm in Norfolk town (7)
10 Aid to electronic music ends in this noisy din with the magnitude right? (11)
13 Drunk son heads off after minute (7)
15 Way of walking to consider, we hear, in entrance (7)
17 America proficient and operational (6)
20 Party with endlessly wealthy Greek order (5)
21 At home, Poles have drinks here? (4)

81

Across

6 Major road with cross raised confusion (3-2)
7 Different people beginning to help in new store (6)
9 Religious book or songs (7)
10 Want to dance after 100! (5)
11 Unisex garment not hot in secret society (4)
13 Eastern European and Irish turn back as competitors (6)
15 Some domestic, a junior Louisiana resident (5)
16 Study again on area that's invested in wine (6)
17 Greek favoured smile (4)
20 Thing moving in dark? (5)
22 Old university lecturer in search for unit of charge (7)
23 Proceeds from ground mince? Around nothing! (6)
24 Vulgar course of action followed by unknown character (5)

Down

1 Former underground worker besieges a tester (8)
2 Point in dictionary is chosen (5)
3 Nearly all keeping one damp (5)
4 Confirming largely airport registration (5-2)
5 Killer whale kept in poor captivity (4)
6 Grim notion confused following (10)
8 New Orleans bay is treated sensibly (10)
12 Blue hues adorn housing (3)
13 Odd percussion instrument lacking depth (3)
14 Display strength in military unit (3,5)
15 Cut short ringing alternate iron weapon with spikes (7)
18 Longed for new head around college (5)
19 Regulated number in half passages (5)
21 Medal obtained in running on grass (4)

82

Across

1 Rule accepted by mug in ridiculous display (5)
4 Woman worried in argument (6)
10 An overdue awkward undertaking (9)
11 Upper-class South Africa – or another country (inits) (3)
12 Dons excited about energy in points in network (5)
13 Enthuse European standing below tree (4,2)
14 Short technical description with mixed mortar and hint of grit produces type of image (11)
18 Boiling sauna contains European sickness (6)
20 Little monkey holds fruit (5)
23 Greek character mostly tense (3)
24 Risky HIV bloke's Marxist (9)
25 Recent way adopted by the Navy (6)
26 Deli vandalized before day was inactive? (5)

Down

2 Fantastic idea daughter supported (5)
3 Sort in charge in noted horserace (7)
5 Troublesome child losing time makes blunder (5)
6 American rocket with a carpet next to University of Los Angeles (7)
7 Largely delete long periods (4)
8 Name plugging beef, say, that's intended (5)
9 Colt farm boy trained in easy fashion (11)
15 Pestered with Black Death, say, and died (7)
16 Festivity experienced for celebrated knight (7)
17 Oriental beverage involves new wind (5)
19 Old boy in series is serious (5)
21 Contend after short time to see film (5)
22 Check feature of wineglass (4)

83

Across

1 Threatens with one hiding inside organizations (6)
5 Make off from city in wet (6)
8 Persian ruler engulfed by clash ahead (4)
9 Suggesting island politician is supported by dishonesty (8)
10 Some fear a bicultural language (6)
11 Breaks open sculptures? About right (6)
12 Ingenuity protecting right in legal document (4)
14 Man who is regularly emigrating (3)
15 Impertinent talk in boys as suspects (4)
16 Forceful chant about Turkey (6)
18 Pair left in two-door car (6)
20 Steffi's healthy one – the writing's on the wall (8)
22 Messenger rejecting old resentful feeling (4)
23 Commercials around last month for mature people (6)
24 Castro upset performers (6)

Down

2 Alternative trouble with bishop missing (5)
3 Check greeting? Bin it perhaps outwardly (7)
4 Changing two bridge players, uncomfortable sensation (9)
5 Princess softly dressing (3)
6 In Cyprus, old monarch is more shy (5)
7 Record of meeting in tiny society (7)
11 Fine porcelain, individual feature in national airline (4,5)
13 Having finished work, out for the night? (7)
15 Pupil getting two poor grades in difficult performance (7)
17 Tripe from Irish county mostly (5)
19 Learner remaining is Juliet, perhaps (5)
21 Those elected gain seats partly (3)

84

Across

1 Designation with extremes of levity to be specific (6)
4 Outcome with two fellows in English city on time (6)
8 It measures power levels in rebellion (3)
9 Leaving trade pure after exchange (9)
11 Twisted nail put in a horizontal position (4)
12 Proclaim a new type of word with Anglicans (8)
15 Teach girl that's disorganized and sluggish (9)
18 Pope's response about writing (8)
19 Classic tales start with this, previously? (4)
21 Service I've left by year largely (9)
23 Ruin drive on way back (3)
24 Note about part of bird in sudden pain (6)
25 More short trees swaying round river (6)

Down

1 Important person, conservative but not posh? A little bit (6)
2 Items pull strange groups (9)
3 Heard cargo layer (4)
5 Leave of absence created by fluff next to Irish lake (8)
6 Bird in match not delayed (3)
7 At last, messenger has no right subjects (6)
10 Fruit seen as long and mottled bar the top (9)
13 Prisons contain sadly mean terms of contempt? (9)
14 In urgent need as a consumer? (8)
16 Instigate computer question (6)
17 More miserly – and less distant? (6)
20 Ditch in Normandy kept (4)
22 Monkey from South American island (3)

Across

8 Speculates visitor docked back half of horses (7)
9 About now, yard is prepared (5)
10 All express impatience? It recurs (5)
11 Order home in journey (7)
12 Sovereign state congress for Chequers, perhaps (7,5)
16 Treat differently indirect aims that are formulated (12)
20 No longer fresh rice cooked for policeman, say (7)
23 Old woman and doctor love Latin American dance (5)
24 Confirm definitely at home relations? (3,2)
25 Chosen without leader in parliament? (7)

Down

1 Ornamental stone in a door, perhaps (5)
2 Ruins 500 oysters, potentially (8)
3 Designate a symbol, we hear (6)
4 Addict in American hospital department (4)
5 Tense and harsh in gutter (6)
6 Large carpet covered by lookalike (4)
7 Kind group prepared for printing (7)
13 Aspect of sleep in threadbare motels (inits) (3)
14 Last university altering MA title (8)
15 Foolish African dictator with religious books in charge (7)
17 Withdraw park worker (6)
18 Perhaps, one anaesthetic (6)
19 Argument over limits to debts in parts of speech (5)
21 Charlatan, a King in France and Spain (4)
22 Bird overhead partly (4)

Across

8 Escort addict around hospital (5)
9 Dressed skin putting European in agitated state (7)
10 Old penny and shilling for mushrooms (7)
11 Rise in society with grand school (3,2)
12 Eccentrics have personal hygiene issue, awful in shame (9)
14 Provide thickness (3)
15 Retiree in TV staple initially overlooked (inits) (3)
16 Paying attention to single hint, not hard, when reviewed (9)
19 Playful odd lout with 599 (5)
21 Goes round old gallery in Royal Society (7)
23 Great ape in difficulty behind river in Indian island (7)
24 Noted dog in quiet Bedfordshire town mostly (5)

Down

1 Excellent person in underwater vessel (6)
2 Dice twice as fast as possible (4-4)
3 Bird's original returned, about right (4)
4 Ascending small mountain with mother and hot gas (6)
5 Big points for generosity (8)
6 Scottish inventor discussed question (4)
7 Attempt to finish inside, fashionable (6)
13 Spy deciphered clue in compound (8)
14 Information from computer with newspaper on strike? (8)
15 Big Leo troubled in bind? (6)
17 A division of pupils in river (6)
18 Industrial protest among Oslo workers maintained (2-4)
20 Cleaners remove it in scandal (4)
22 See on return upper body wear (4)

Across

1 Remainder of rum chaps put close to beermat (7)
5 Examine strewn cans (4)
10 Teacher's footwear (7)
11 Motionless at home, periodically regret (5)
12 Test provided dominant theme (5)
13 Call for further performance in Parisian centre (6)
15 Rub out two notes on dial (6)
17 Some schemer generally to come into view (6)
19 Clean space devoid of air (6)
20 Fierce cat, thing heard in odd places (5)
23 By the sound of it, quiet musical composition (5)
24 Most expansive ten logs reviewed (7)
25 Back of neck seen in Northern primate (4)
26 Views features (7)

Down

2 Traded in man-made alternatives (5)
3 Chap having designed future car is industrialist (12)
4 Tends to hurry back over steps oddly (6)
6 More obvious article from France held by domestic worker (7)
7 Captures features in tennis (4)
8 Obstructs institute in system requiring reform (7)
9 Event, travelling show entertains 1000 with brown hollow circle (12)
14 Inscribe again note on legal document, English (7)
16 Distress signal on high for outbreak (5-2)
18 Two lakes in terrible mess producing odours (6)
21 Recipient of hospitality in rogue's tavern (5)
22 Second item of verbal wit favourably presented (4)

Across

1 Paces made by top players infused with power (6)
4 Place in ship with a big German gun (6)
9 Football team ending that's partly outdated (abbr) (3)
10 Name phone that's reproduced remarkable things (9)
11 Language fair in review about Sweden (5)
12 Cardinal's confused without Nationalist extremist (7)
14 Sets up time in New York with man in a joyful state (11)
17 Lettuce seen near the poles? (7)
18 One's togetherness (5)
20 Stakes in hobbies (9)
22 Graduate with a bleat (3)
23 Concealed place for thrashing (6)
24 Parting words in promotion that is American (6)

Down

1 Good man with pair of fellows in America practises taxidermy (6)
2 Metal joiner's topless senior figure (5)
3 Fold copy (9)
5 Lemon-filling, musical style (3)
6 Excessive sentimentality? Trace cultivated by the French (7)
7 Reportedly, a head covering to be of use (5)
8 Medical expert ignores lout after disruption (11)
13 Inspector's sworn? It's put under examination (9)
15 Toiled with seat we'd broken (7)
16 Major operation in relief road (6)
17 Flower in front of hotel in Dublin? (5)
19 I'm sad without novice to instil (5)
21 Manage to move quickly (3)

Across

6 Shows bottom with low, new section (5)
7 Stops first of excursionists blocking luggage (6)
9 Determined duke behind bench (7)
10 Giant bird beginning to arc north (5)
11 Supplemented element in parade kept back (4)
13 Name I misplaced when embracing old Bond actress (6)
15 Influence reporting of cats and dogs? (5)
16 Prophet misled in deal (6)
17 Measure of resistance in old British ship (4)
20 Sister runs off close to home (5)
22 Celebrated atmosphere about Spanish drink (7)
23 Black lining produces traveller's irritation (3,3)
24 Fellow in education given penalty (5)

Down

1 Norse hut reconstructed – coming from warmer climes? (8)
2 Extra note before a Latin mass in devotional song (5)
3 Crosses swiftly food chewed on board (5)
4 Alien inhabitant moving in a tram (7)
5 Agitated about a fever (4)
6 Deceptive dealings I'm to alter (10)
8 Make out beneath stadium (10)
12 Hair accessory to begin to work (3)
13 Navy run Red Cross, for example (inits) (3)
14 Hotel in a marina built for Indian prince's wife (8)
15 Shows meat in reserve (7)
18 Custom in Prohibition? (5)
19 Stab King – fine mess! (5)
21 Backward look in dance (4)

90

Across

1 Requested a schedule (5)
4 Pal is excited touring city that's distinctive (7)
9 Joke about a home, mostly Asian (8)
10 Heads of York and Cheshire Kayakers prattle on (4)
11 Service cycles with one chief accountant in continent (6)
12 Supply internet joke? (5)
13 Lake found in former estate (4)
15 Shade is massive, not good (3)
16 Some pastures toured in tranquility (4)
17 Begin record (5)
19 Tried fashion with Dior's first (6)
21 Eye greedily some grog left (4)
22 Organized branches in periods of history? (8)
23 Attack Biblical convert in a sudden torment initially (7)
24 Instant tea and coffee (5)

Down

2 Stick for teachers? (5)
3 Investigate and dismiss revolutionary source (7)
5 Strangely interfere with lap that's biased (12)
6 Aquatic rodent making unusual copy for all to see (5)
7 Receives a county councillor on step awkwardly (7)
8 Emphatic oral works are figurative (12)
14 Issues seem to vary about measure of work (7)
16 Retired gentleman with German getting Italian dish (7)
18 Article on Central America in case (5)
20 Hide soil (5)

Across

8 Very cool crocodile snapped without reproductive organs, at first (3-4)
9 A team getting prestigious award? It's indisputably true (5)
10 Goodbye unoriginal wireless receivers! (5)
11 Talented runner, fellow in quiet period mostly (7)
12 Now appropriate skill becomes resourcefulness (12)
16 Bit policeman disputed is not consistent (12)
20 Tool for bridge? (7)
23 Fault about old tenor, say (5)
24 Excitable astronomer secures minimum (5)
25 See river competition (7)

Down

1 Last part of stuff in a lodge (5)
2 Endless oil priced poorly? It's occasional (8)
3 Chat is so varied when detained by doctor (6)
4 Sets of rules not caught in poems (4)
5 Slate small headless Italian sandwiches (6)
6 Repeated musical phrase encapsulated by trumpeter if followed (4)
7 Uses European money on manoeuvres (7)
13 Area north of Virginia at all in Scotland? (3)
14 Poorly regulated and inopportune (3-5)
15 Without Princess and son, discharges prayer books (7)
17 Extremely small part of an hour (6)
18 Devise at home opening (6)
19 End hated sadly (5)
21 Unfastened Indian prince rises (4)
22 Strain in timeless recorded music (4)

Across

1 Rally eg dispersed to a great extent (7)
5 Half vintaged and matured (4)
9 Western painter's stands showing mammals (7)
10 Speaks, ask later, holds back (5)
11 Unyielding rear of vessel (5)
12 Feeling of irritation in knitting accessory (6)
14 Boffin reported increased productivity in hens? (6)
16 Solidify and stand still (6)
18 Criticizes reversals (6)
19 Panel recalling Italian island with time (5)
22 Number in cognitive therapy (5)
23 Most of relative has snake – let go! (7)
24 Year with fuss backing Star Wars character (4)
25 Eggy mixture covers toolbox evenly with study of stones (7)

Down

2 Conscious conflict is found in Austria and Spain (5)
3 Dealer in cookers perhaps (11)
4 Missing error in diary (6)
6 Biblical town around Israel confused eagle (7)
7 Mercedes key engulfs work surface (4)
8 Distorted wit's funny in unruly teenager (7)
10 Academic gold alien in chalet I constructed (11)
13 Queen returns to church with one personal trainer voucher (7)
15 Haggard companion breaking long day (7)
17 Give confidence to fool on river (6)
20 Belgium to suspend drug (5)
21 Quite clever youth boxing (4)

93

Across

8 First person's intention expressed in part of supermarket (5)
9 Result from striking approach (7)
10 I retain mysterious lack of movement (7)
11 Attach to military unit journalist holding award (5)
12 Note house with British woman (9)
14 One learned in education in renowned department (inits) (3)
15 Fake fish (3)
16 Praising driver once with politician (9)
19 Part of dishonesty glowed (5)
21 Cusses angrily about Catholic happiness (7)
23 Confusion of a mature enthusiast (7)
24 Bandage despicably envelops (5)

Down

1 North America struggles to supply maritime forces (6)
2 Admired point on horse carrying me (8)
3 Annoying kind scrapes tomato sandwiches (4)
4 Spot maturity in senility (6)
5 Unusual Finn isn't present at exciting Internet Cafe, and so on (2,6)
6 Explosive device a flop (4)
7 Element extremely experienced characterising some petrol? (6)
13 Religious sort always behind British priest (8)
14 Store ice erratically? It's puzzling (8)
15 Negligent occasional worker (6)
17 University nurse working without certainty (6)
18 Toady starts to enjoy service among many possibly (3-3)
20 Roughly round cricket ground (4)
22 Cyprus stumped for growth (4)

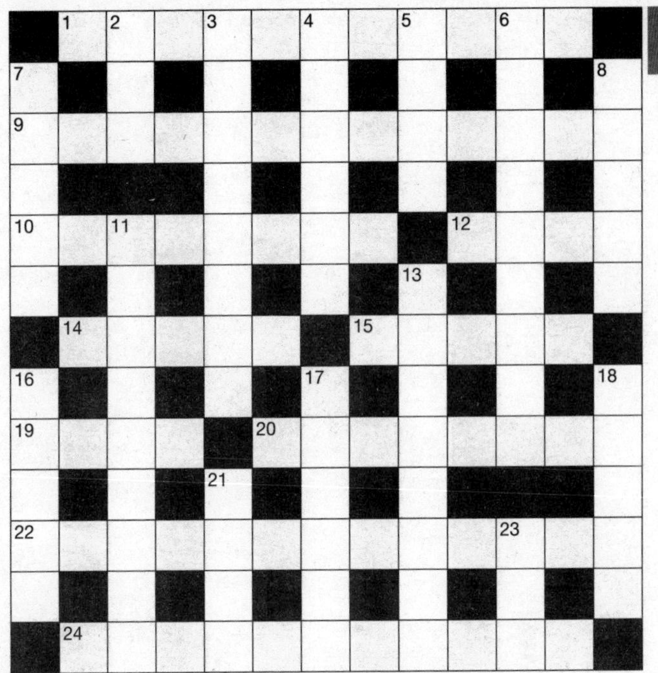

94

Across

1 Unwillingness to accept one clarinet when played (11)
9 NUT are guarded about student (13)
10 Crude gin simmers, thickening (8)
12 Grey like a tree? (4)
14 Type round piano for enjoyment (5)
15 Noted cricketer's elegance (5)
19 Called some trader angrily (4)
20 Prophetic speaking about copper and argon (8)
22 Unusual ally, judge in Bahamas generally regarded (2,3,8)
24 Is it last act possibly dealing with numerical facts? (11)

Down

2 Evenly unload and agree (3)
3 Coroner ordered date to be officially declared (2,6)
4 Managed in English road assignment (6)
5 Promotes benefits (4)
6 Traditional group in charge with a learner (9)
7 Posh bishop entering Hungary's borders in rush (5)
8 Woman's precious stone (5)
11 Child, maybe, starts to drape excitedly flag (9)
13 Sibling caught weird coil in vegetable (8)
16 Brit is stirred by European family (5)
17 King reportedly in ruins (6)
18 Solid danger not fully apparent in afternoon (5)
21 Fifty in bed solidify (4)
23 Northern attorney gets contract enforcing secrecy (inits) (3)

95

Across

6 It ensures straightness for monarch perhaps (5)
7 Afternoon in Scottish valleys picks up (6)
9 Type of logic in ghostly shout on bend (7)
10 Criminal is one in racket (5)
11 Flower I left in large yard (4)
13 Small lock of hair in tension (6)
15 I love time playing Greek characters (5)
16 Disgrace in stateless family (6)
17 Atmospheric element in new age (4)
20 Harmful radiation with middle of bulb, a thing found at the back of the throat (5)
22 Money in Berlin, say (7)
23 Corrupt Petty Officer is no revolutionary (6)
24 Second politician in tale (5)

Down

1 Cello at work, fine component in music? (4,4)
2 Withered medic that is head of dermatology (5)
3 Previously New York has pain (5)
4 Paltry sum of money for bar snack (7)
5 Opponent is a fool getting early end (4)
6 Defiant about gong with promises (10)
8 Prose crafted by Northern friend subjectively (10)
12 Note yen for bean (3)
13 Escape regularly method for returning mail (inits) (3)
14 Event in which people show crosses? (8)
15 Young troublemaker and fool close to tense stalemate (7)
18 Landscape is observed, we hear (5)
19 Sudden contraction in resort's money (5)
21 Awake and working over (4)

Across

7 Young cat goes round woman's innocent child (6)
8 Surge atop reed (6)
9 Part of taste test – leave unaltered (4)
10 En route – or about to arrive? (2,3,3)
11 Trustworthy figure shows this concerning debt (11)
14 Eccentric is tense with friend basically (11)
18 Aquatic animal quiet in habitat (8)
19 Grey Estate hides organs (4)
20 Record by American in athletics event (6)
21 Preserve cooked lamb after English meal's beginning (6)

Down

1 Atmosphere mentioned in expression of doubt? (7)
2 First sign of detested deserter brings exasperated cry (4)
3 Receive a circle touring Bahamas (6)
4 Deadly ethic about first bit of teaching (6)
5 Generate new drink (5,3)
6 NASA worked around one from Tokyo, perhaps (5)
12 Teach in trust working around Cuba (8)
13 Old like a tree? (7)
15 Reveal experience with operating system, electronic (6)
16 Meat prepared around North Dakota for two? (6)
17 Worth in former itinerary (5)
19 Breadth in English book society declines (4)

Across

1 Permits a line by quiet soprano (6)
4 Volume finished and sold (6)
9 Broadcast heard in Scottish city (3)
10 Beam of light enfolds oculus designed in a harsh way (9)
11 Took in old Conservative politician in audience (5)
12 Commanded and tidied (7)
14 Unusual malice? It's in uses of violence etc (11)
17 Most vile inventions in tug at sea (7)
18 Don't begin to feel sorry for a heron (5)
20 At home, curtailed spirit of you and me is astute (9)
22 Oil company on island showing computing measure in short (inits) (3)
23 Frenchman in parlour gets fish (6)
24 Inquiry when head of state? (6)

Down

1 Lack of interest in a route close to city (6)
2 Immature state in regular vagrant (5)
3 Global news about pound and extra (9)
5 Environmentally friendly city on ocean's front (3)
6 Merit of French tennis player's shot (7)
7 Boring promotion for nymph (5)
8 Unable to work – and excluded from engagement? (3,2,6)
13 Cuts back and irons? (9)
15 Unwell say on a lake – it's not allowed! (7)
16 Hang rope series (6)
17 Comes together without energy for items (5)
19 Religious teacher to chat endlessly (5)
21 Oddly, nachos make a soldier! (inits) (3)

98

Across

8 Money from Cuba put into attraction (5)
9 Unity feasible with European head (7)
10 Article in house that's plain (7)
11 Deadhead more quickly flower (5)
12 Put out again piquant sauce around bar (9)
14 Pull from East presumably? (3)
15 A boss lacking overly large muscles (3)
16 Extremely poor rise with blame dished out (9)
19 Oxygen I inhale contains spirits (5)
21 Fumigate forcefully, evicting leading mites with lethargy (7)
23 Large book in store reviewed crustacean (7)
24 Pursue drink with small earl (5)

Down

1 Smart Conservative with crowbar (6)
2 Pints chaps ordered having missed it as strong alcoholic drink (8)
3 Sense payment left (4)
4 Well, Timbuktu's country produces someone from Mogadishu (6)
5 Harm poet created in figure of speech (8)
6 Relish orange peel (4)
7 Legal deed more serious in turn about college (6)
13 Happen to meet worthless horse (4,4)
14 Gabon got defective sledge (8)
15 Financial backers for nurses (6)
17 Expedition in the distance in southern island (6)
18 Flattened Biblical lady and Biblical Simpson (6)
20 VIPs, elitist head to tail (4)
22 Electronic equipment in educational institute (4)

99

Across

1 Wait on a tense nurse (6)
5 Take car north in very motivated way (6)
8 Wife on every barrier (4)
9 Hated Princess, Saint enjoyed (8)
10 As a gamble, nuclear ship is kept by oil powers? (2,4)
11 Noted fellow with a computing device largely (6)
12 Sword hidden in tepees (4)
14 Disowns taking every other particle (3)
15 Sheep from East and West largely (4)
16 Keep thanks in check (6)
18 Stops sailor, mixed sort (6)
20 Limit break taken by tiny US state court (8)
22 Repulsive bow tie director discarded (4)
23 Top actor getting extremely envious looks (6)
24 Bird an Arab located in Cyprus (6)

Down

2 Direct series (5)
3 Hide partially pieces of footage in middle of reel (7)
4 Notice dud working to get inference (9)
5 Formal wear for radio entertainers (abbr) (3)
6 One princess has award for phrase (5)
7 Carry out powerful businessman on pick-up vehicle (7)
11 Brilliant supporter cast it in a different way (9)
13 Gift is here (7)
15 Electronic proposal? Joy, for instance! (7)
17 Stern monarch at a later time (5)
19 One accepting offer in cargo ship, not new (5)
21 American tax office first loses its margins (inits) (3)

Across

1 It's used for winding film showcasing initially indoor game (5)
4 Motives in logic by son (7)
9 Jumbo is the plane requiring renovation (8)
10 Travellers in Cairo marry (4)
11 Unintelligent investigator kept by boss (6)
12 Figure doffing hat in dark shade (5)
13 Hot-feeling mop? (4)
15 English bishops in decline (3)
16 Trio of lecturers stopped by university getting period of rest (4)
17 Revolutionary name embracing hard set of principles (5)
19 Minor actors included in text rashly (6)
21 Burden on island in cab (4)
22 Upright character in transcribed Latin is providing evidence of agreement? (8)
23 Put right festering rift round city yard (7)
24 Oversee some part of poem (5)

Down

2 Steer sanctimonious group (5)
3 Theoretically concerning Times, for instance (2,5)
5 Admit one's error putting part of hand into English drink and food (3,6,3)
6 Woody plant from river hidden by wild bush (5)
7 Carelessly run male figure (7)
8 Around start of day crave principal costume accessory (12)
14 Standard state over long period (7)
16 Highly positioned room kept by the French network (7)
18 This criminal is infused with energy in robbery (5)
20 Set of maps finally shortened (5)

101

Across

1 Idea previously source of problems in court (7)
5 Stage in graph as explained (5)
9 Worsening trade ie with root in reforms (13)
10 Supplies and removes key organs? (8)
11 Large book intended for writer? (4)
12 Narrow ravine split Holy Mother and gadgetry (9)
16 Ask possibly after year for long-haired cattle (4)
17 Book, depressing throughout, to fade in time (4,4)
19 A third's priced wrongly for one carrying items (8,5)
21 Comes across hunting events (5)
22 A canine expert? (7)

Down

2 Conformed to award the old Duke (6)
3 Chic males developed compounds (9)
4 Group of lions was nosy, we hear (5)
6 Small dwelling enclosed by shutters (3)
7 Peak month on board ship for tempests (6)
8 What's happened is in stadium largely (6)
11 Mistake is found in middle of letter for cell member? (9)
13 Routines with a couple of hard parts (6)
14 Style of humour that's seated with anger (6)
15 Outcasts drive back, rising up on society (6)
18 Scottish expression of regret about earthy pigment (5)
20 Favourite cat say (3)

102

Across

1 Hideout in road recalled in legal actions (6)
4 Wise men keeping time in periods (6)
8 Lunatic teachers' union (3)
9 Sample prepared forest tea (9)
11 Arab chieftain taken in by some miracle (4)
12 Obvious jump over axe (5-3)
15 Regular habit in odd places? That's doubtful (9)
18 Composer lifting function, single male (8)
19 Injury in part of Spanish armada (4)
21 Evaluation: outrage, full of endless praise (9)
23 Avoiding pressure, omit winter sports item (3)
24 More ingenuous backward priest, Scotsman (6)
25 Wade, ashen, across large cups (6)

Down

1 Leonard with enthusiast back in underground passage (6)
2 Mixed ricin isn't essential (9)
3 Quit – not right (4)
5 Roman Catholic amid threat mobilized Roman governor (8)
6 Soldiers, partly biologists (abbr) (3)
7 Quantity of paper man kept in groups (6)
10 Statements of aunts and uncles, say (9)
13 Renovated old places fell down (9)
14 Make some DNA and judge (8)
16 Secure a bit on bananas (6)
17 Single Frenchman with vest gets energy drink (6)
20 Pest to run away, it's said (4)
22 Quiet greeting for Greek character (3)

Across

1 Elvish ritual at first transformed into contract (7)
5 In window, I spot thin strand (4)
10 Side branches with TVs not being used? (7)
11 Sold five less and closed (5)
12 Evergreen shrub almost blooming in marshy outlet (5)
13 Diamonds left in New York courteously (6)
15 Sailed at sea showing perfect standards (6)
17 Production of film, some classic in emancipation (6)
19 Mixed notice for intellectual (6)
20 Stealing article in front of paper (5)
23 Animated boxer with source of vital energy (5)
24 Old books I caught by a set of foreign objects (7)
25 Car with valuation in even places (4)
26 Ruins successes (7)

Down

2 Sizeable fellow blocking the untidy yard (5)
3 Alien is quiet when battling social injustices? (12)
4 Relaxing start to Easter? A sign possibly (6)
6 Favour eluding eccentric (7)
7 Cases in schools (4)
8 Study book on port displaying liveliness (3,4)
9 Consider tips for moving portrayals (12)
14 Fellow with genuine description of a documentary? (7)
16 Tit goes all over the place for self-absorbed person (7)
18 Shriek in irresistibly funny person (6)
21 Cream in back of fridge, low in calories (5)
22 Mother in Massachusetts twice (4)

104

Across

1 Rug by high school for school subject? (5)
4 Powerless and insecure without saint (6)
10 Devil? It was worshipped by Philistines (9)
11 Some current source of light left out (3)
12 Teacher in varied tour round Thailand (5)
13 Boy don trained, insignificant type (6)
14 Pop group – where we might find dogs with lads? (3,4,4)
18 Shapes jellies? (6)
20 Come round with note on low fellow (5)
23 Short month in the centre of Hanover (abbr) (3)
24 Concocted alibi with connections is evidence of talent (9)
25 Urges approaches (6)
26 Sign of cold British TV interviewer (5)

Down

2 Able US lawyer held up over record time (5)
3 Arizona surrounded by harsh and primarily severe threats (7)
5 A book kept by upper-class sort, very wealthy type (5)
6 Eventually alongside mulled brandy, not right (2,3,2)
7 Show in index posting (4)
8 Assists old US President thus discontented (5)
9 A group in hops at sea take emergency action there? (7,4)
15 Grows, on reflection, to adore clothing, mostly (7)
16 Lawyer ignoring street obstacle (7)
17 Caught corrosion in outer layer (5)
19 Rent artist's stand with bottom raised (5)
21 Steals keys as aid for students (5)
22 Cut bargain (4)

SOLUTIONS

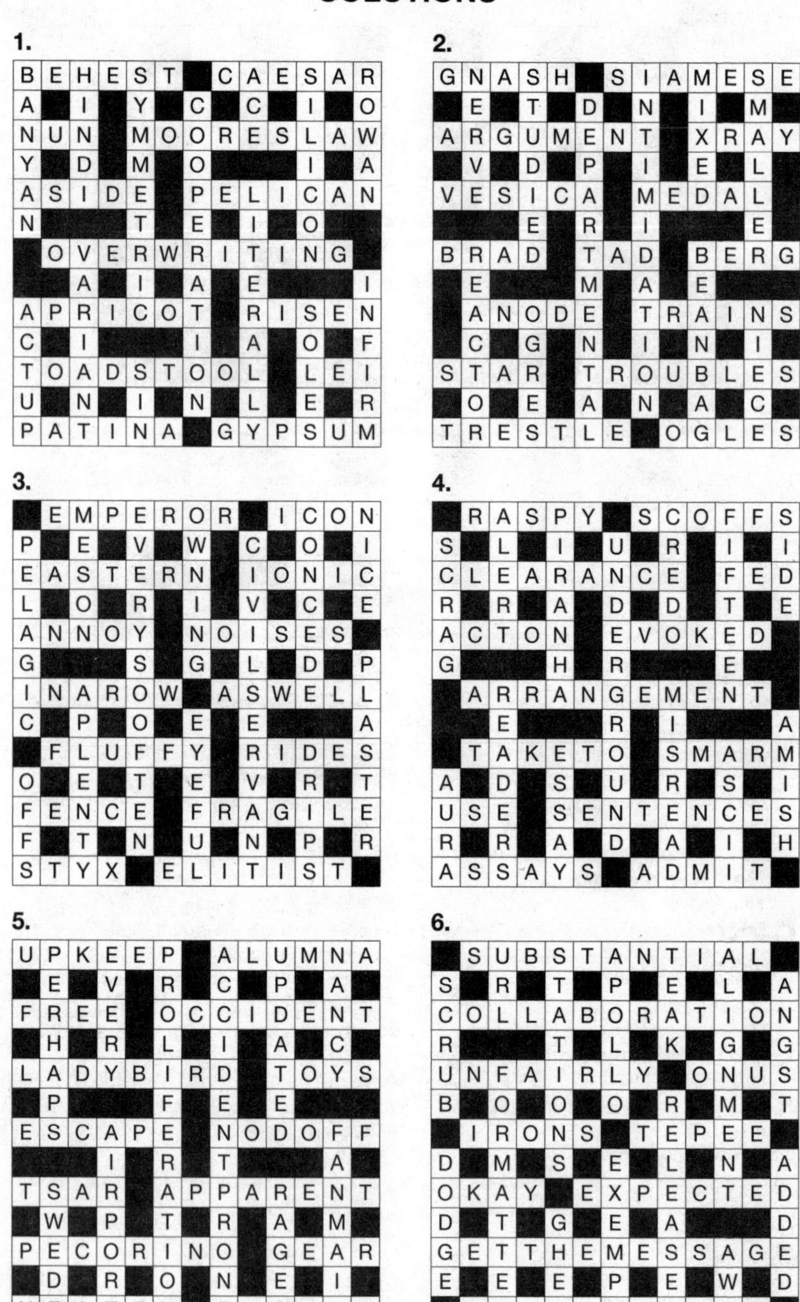

SOLUTIONS

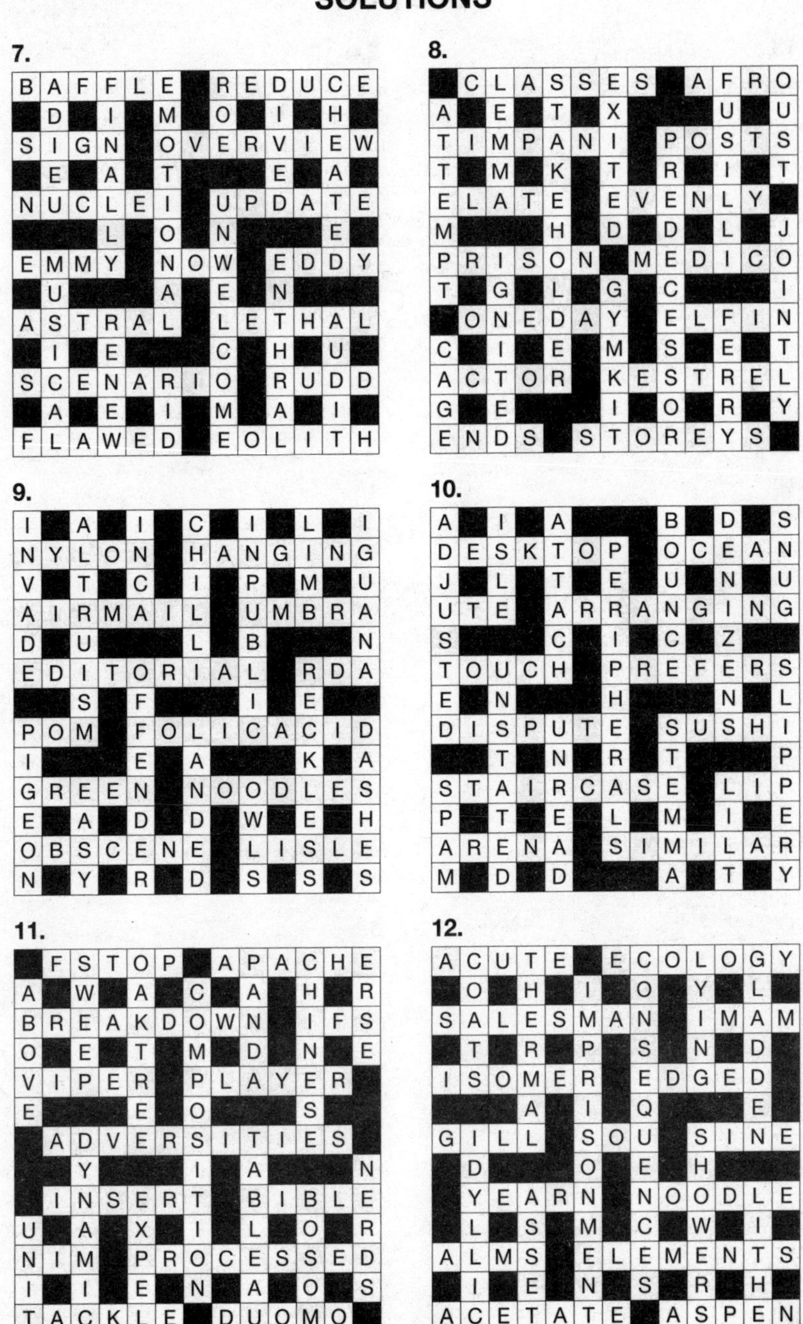

SOLUTIONS

13.

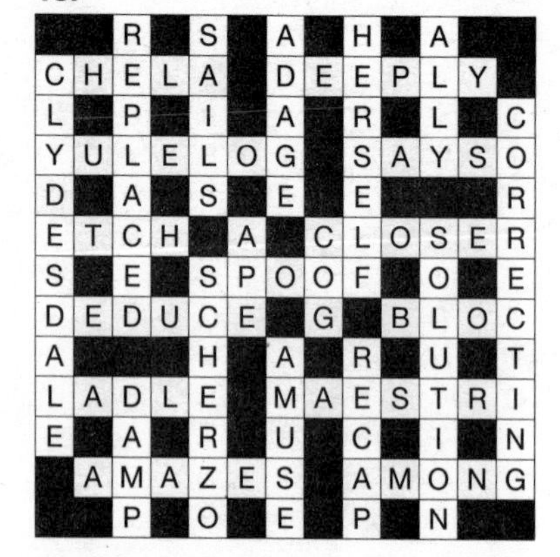

		R		S		A		H		A		
C	H	E	L	A		D	E	E	P	L	Y	
L		P		I		A		R		L		C
Y	U	L	E	L	O	G		S	A	Y	S	O
D		A		S		E		E				R
E	T	C	H		A		C	L	O	S	E	R
S		E		S	P	O	O	F		O		E
D	E	D	U	C	E		G		B	L	O	C
A				H		A		R		U		T
L	A	D	L	E		M	A	E	S	T	R	I
E		A		R		U		C		I		N
	A	M	A	Z	E	S		A	M	O	N	G
		P		O		E		P		N		

14.

A	M	I	D		O	U	T	L	O	O	K	S
	I		E		P		O		N		E	
E	S	P	R	I	T		R	E	S	I	G	N
	E		A		I		P		E			
B	R	A	N		C	R	E	A	T	I	V	E
	A		G				D				A	
O	B	J	E	C	T	I	O	N	A	B	L	E
	L				A				C		E	
C	Y	R	I	L	L	I	C		C	E	N	T
			N		E		A		U		T	
S	U	D	D	E	N		M	Y	S	T	I	C
	A		I		T		P		E		N	
R	E	V	E	R	S	E	S		S	P	E	D

15.

R		M		M				S		S		S
O	R	I	G	A	M	I		O	C	T	E	T
A		E		D		M		C		R		U
D	A	N		C	A	P	R	I	C	O	R	N
R				A		R		A		N		
A	D	D	U	P		O	B	L	I	G	E	D
G		A				V				E		I
E	N	F	O	R	C	E		E	A	R	N	S
		F		I		M		I				C
S	P	O	O	N	R	E	S	T		A	D	O
T		D		S		N		H		R		V
A	B	I	D	E		T	H	E	A	T	R	E
G		L		D				R		S		R

16.

R	H	U	B	A	R	B		A	B	Y	S	S
	U		E		E		A		O		C	
I	N	T	H	E	R	E	G	I	O	N	O	F
	G		A		U		R				R	
P	R	O	V	I	N	C	E		M	E	E	K
	Y		I				E		O		D	
		P	O	M	P	O	S	I	T	Y		
	A		U		E				O		F	
P	U	R	R		R	E	S	T	R	A	I	N
	T				M		Y		W		E	
Q	U	E	S	T	I	O	N	N	A	I	R	E
	M		K		T		O		Y		C	
K	N	E	A	D		O	D	Y	S	S	E	Y

17.

G	R	A	N	D	P	A	R	E	N	T	S	
O		D		E		S		N		O		H
L	E	V	E	L		H	I	G	H	T	E	A
D		E		I		R		I				B
S	U	R	F		B	A	R	N	A	C	L	E
T		S		P		M		E		A		A
A	G	E	O	L	D		H	E	A	R	T	S
N		L		A		T		R		B		C
D	A	Y	B	Y	D	A	Y		N	O	N	O
A				B		R		S		N		R
R	E	C	L	A	I	M		C	R	A	M	P
D		U		L		A		A		D		U
	A	P	P	L	I	C	A	T	I	O	N	S

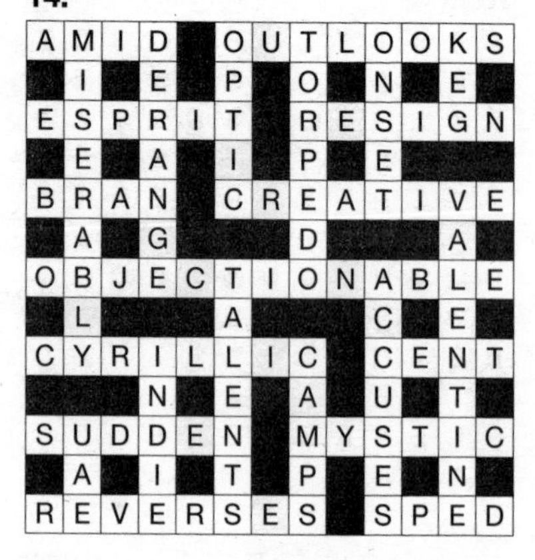

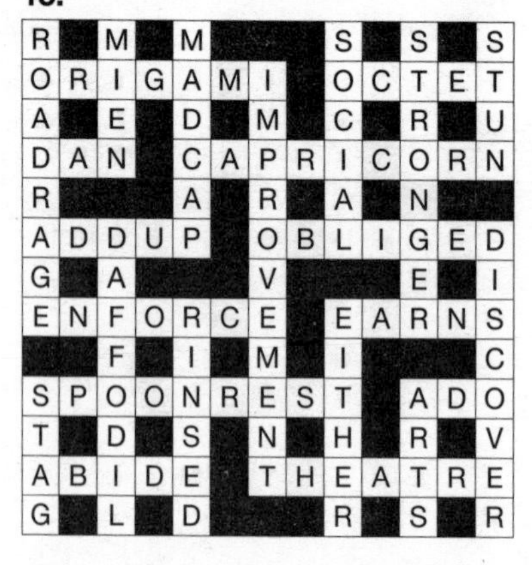

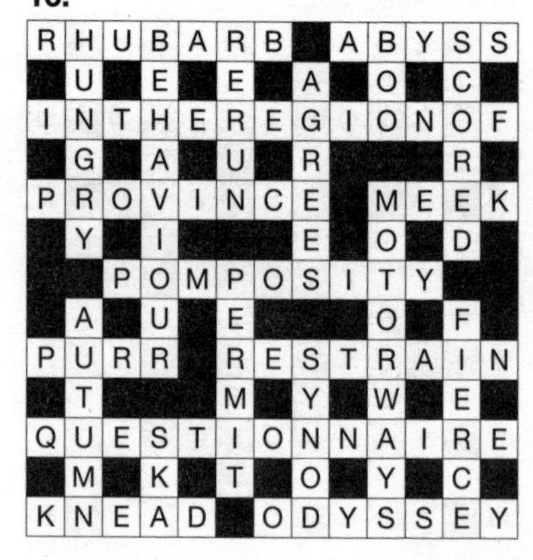

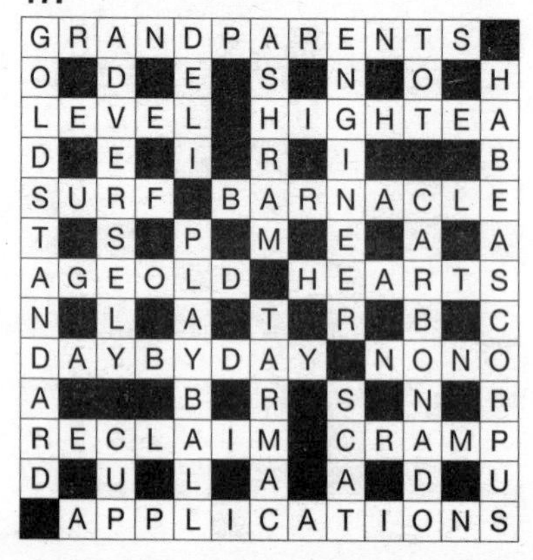

18.

	C		S		J		T		P		A	
G	A	T	E	A	U		O	B	O	I	S	T
	T		E		N		G		S		P	
S	C	U	D		G	O	G	E	T	T	E	R
	H				L		L		P		R	
H	O	B	B	L	E	D	E	H	O	Y		
	N		O						N		A	
		C	O	G	N	O	S	C	E	N	T	I
	T		K		E		Y				T	
M	E	S	S	A	G	E	S		C	R	E	W
	M		H		A		T		U		N	
O	P	T	O	U	T		E	M	B	E	D	S
	T		P		E		M		S		S	

SOLUTIONS

19.

20.

	R	E	P	R	E	S	E	N	T	E	D	
C		A		E		M		E		S		P
A	U	T	O	B	I	O	G	R	A	P	H	Y
U				U		O		D		E		G
S	U	B	S	I	S	T	S		D	R	A	M
E		L		L		H		G		A		Y
	H	A	R	D	Y		L	O	A	N	S	
A		C		S		E		S		T		U
L	I	K	E		E	M	O	T	I	O	N	S
G		S		D		B		E				I
A	P	P	R	O	P	R	I	A	T	I	O	N
E		O		U		Y		D		R		G
	S	T	E	R	E	O	T	Y	P	E	S	

21.

R	E	L	E	A	R	N		B	R	I	N	E
	N		X		A		C		S		U	
C	O	M	P	L	I	C	A	T	I	O	N	S
	U		L		T		S				C	
I	G	N	O	R	A	N	T		C	R	I	B
	H		I				L		L		O	
		S	T	R	A	T	E	G	I	C		
	P		E		I				M		R	
A	R	I	D		D	E	C	L	A	R	E	S
	I				I		O		C		A	
F	E	E	D	I	N	G	B	O	T	T	L	E
	S		O		G		R		I		M	
S	T	A	S	H		S	A	R	C	A	S	M

22.

23.

24.

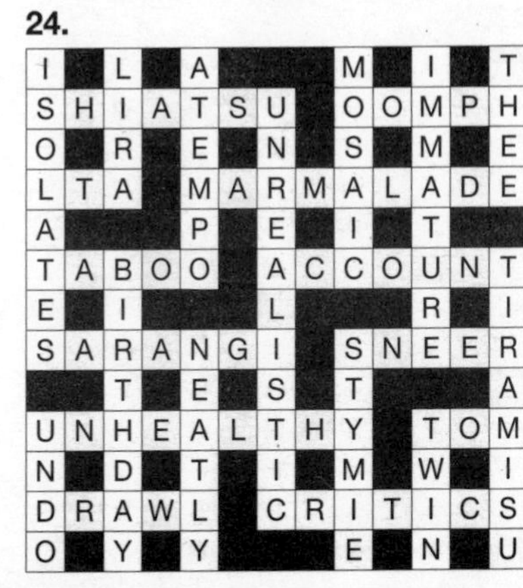

SOLUTIONS

25.

26.

27.

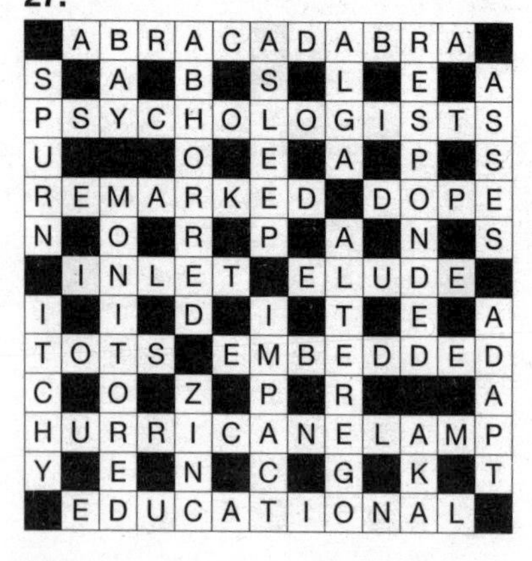

28.

29.

	B	A	N	D	A	N	A		S	T	U	B
W		S		R		O				H		A
E	X	H	A	U	S	T		L	A	U	G	H
I		E		M		I		A		N		T
G	E	N	O	A		C	A	N	A	D	A	
E				N		E		D		E		L
L	I	B	I	D	O		S	I	E	R	R	A
A		I		B		R		N				W
	T	O	M	A	T	O		G	Y	P	S	Y
T		L		S		D		G		I		E
W	O	O	D	S		E	L	E	C	T	O	R
I		G				N		A		T		S
G	U	Y	S		E	T	E	R	N	A	L	

30.

L	A	T	T	E	R		E	N	C	A	M	P
O		U		R				E		R		R
O	U	R		O	R	C	H	E	S	T	R	A
K		N		S		O		D				I
E	A	T	S		A	N	A	L	Y	S	I	S
D		A		A		S		E		E		E
		B	O	T	T	O	M	S	U	P		
D		L		T		N		S		A		A
I	C	E	C	R	E	A	M		C	R	O	C
L				A		N		E		A		C
A	L	L	O	C	A	T	E	D		T	E	E
T		A		T				I		O		S
E	L	D	E	S	T		S	T	O	R	E	S

SOLUTIONS

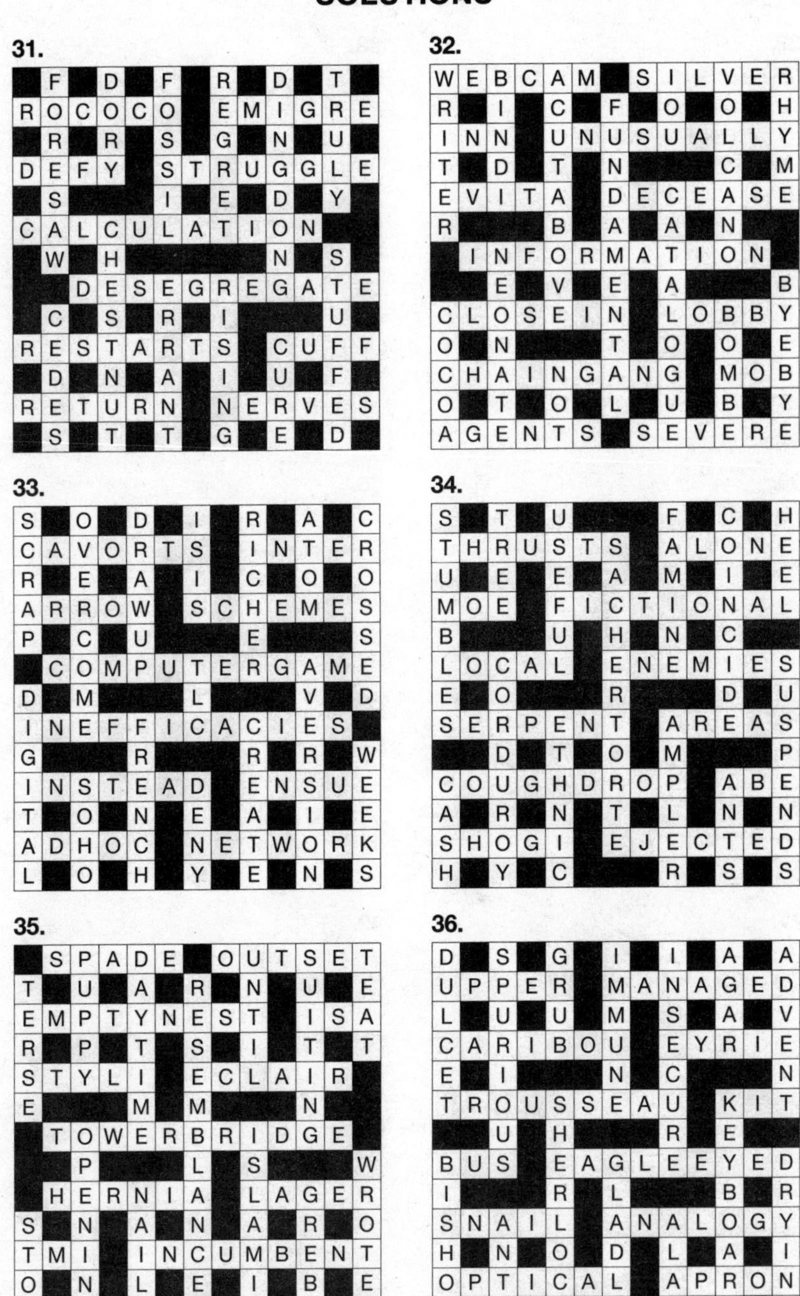

SOLUTIONS

37.

38.

39.

	S		A		G		A		G		R	
R	E	E	C	H	O		V	A	L	U	E	D
	N		H		K		O		A		I	
R	A	R	E		A	C	C	I	D	E	N	T
	T				R		E		I		S	
C	O	M	P	E	T	I	T	I	O	N		
	R		R						L		E	
		R	E	G	U	L	A	T	I	O	N	S
	L		V		N		N				C	
D	E	C	I	S	I	O	N		A	B	L	E
	A		O		T		U		I		O	
A	S	S	U	M	E		A	C	R	O	S	S
	H		S		D		L		S		E	

40.

41.

B	O	T	T	O	M		S	C	O	T	C	H
	D		E		E		A		M		A	
S	O	R	E		N	E	G	L	E	C	T	S
	U		N		T				G		C	
A	R	G	A	L	I		D	E	A	T	H	S
			G		O		A				U	
N	A	V	E		N	I	L		C	O	P	Y
	R				E		M		R			
F	R	I	E	N	D		A	B	U	S	E	D
	I		N				T		I		L	
S	V	E	N	G	A	L	I		S	N	O	B
	E		U		S		A		E		P	
A	D	M	I	T	S		N	O	S	H	E	S

42.

S	P	A	S		S	T	R	I	C	T	L	Y
	A		E		L		E		A		E	
P	S	Y	C	H	E		W	I	N	N	E	R
	S		R		E		R		O			
T	W	E	E		P	R	O	T	E	C	T	S
	O		T				T				H	
C	R	O	S	S	T	H	E	F	L	O	O	R
	D				R				A		U	
T	S	A	R	D	O	M	S		T	E	S	T
			U		U		E		V		A	
H	O	B	N	O	B		R	E	I	G	N	S
	I		I		L		V		A		D	
B	L	A	C	K	E	Y	E		N	E	S	T

SOLUTIONS

43.

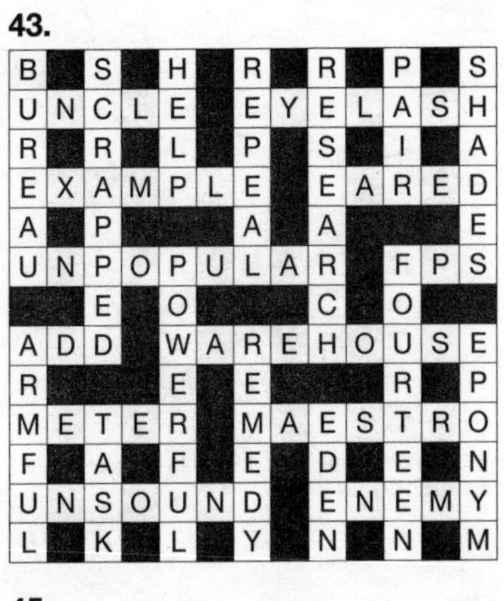

44.

45.

46.

47.

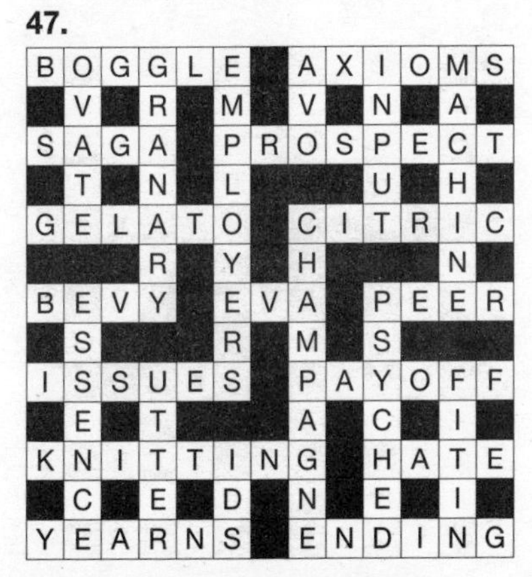

48.

SOLUTIONS

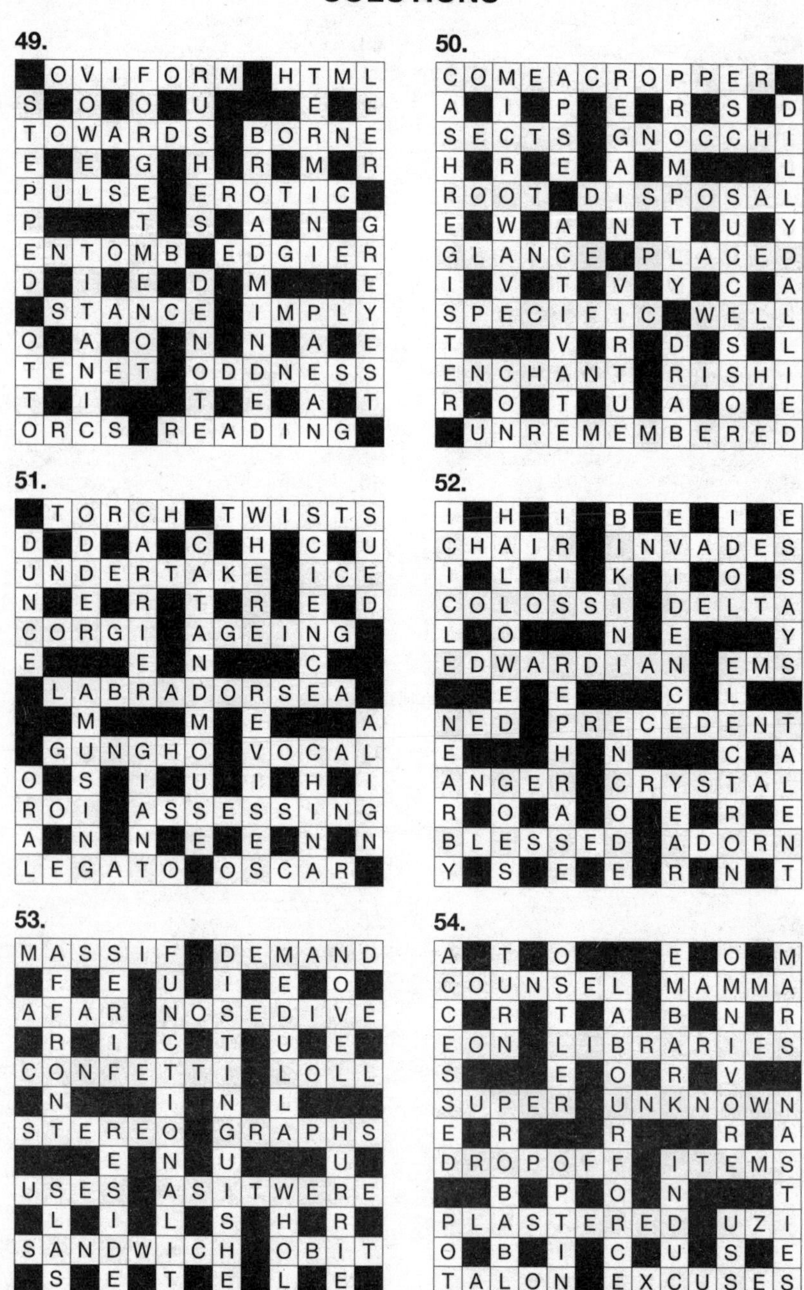

SOLUTIONS

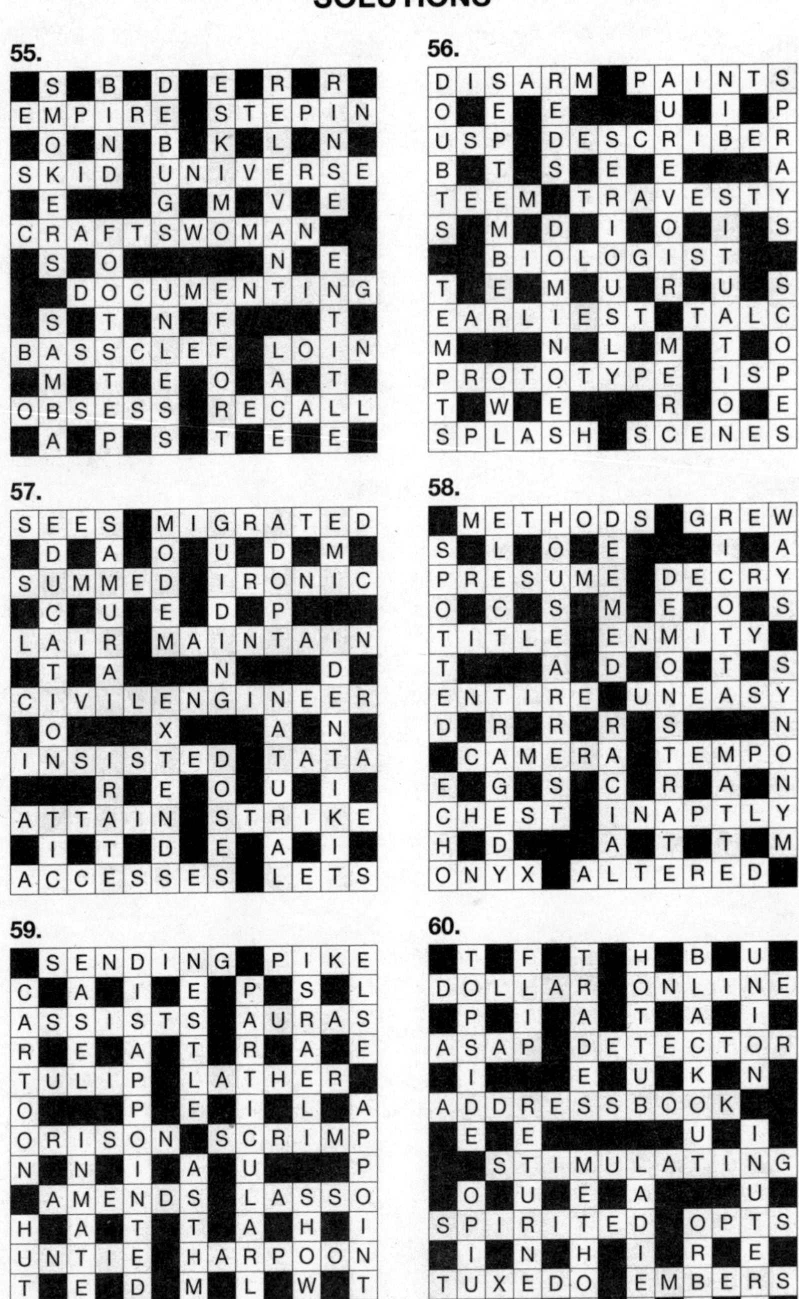

SOLUTIONS

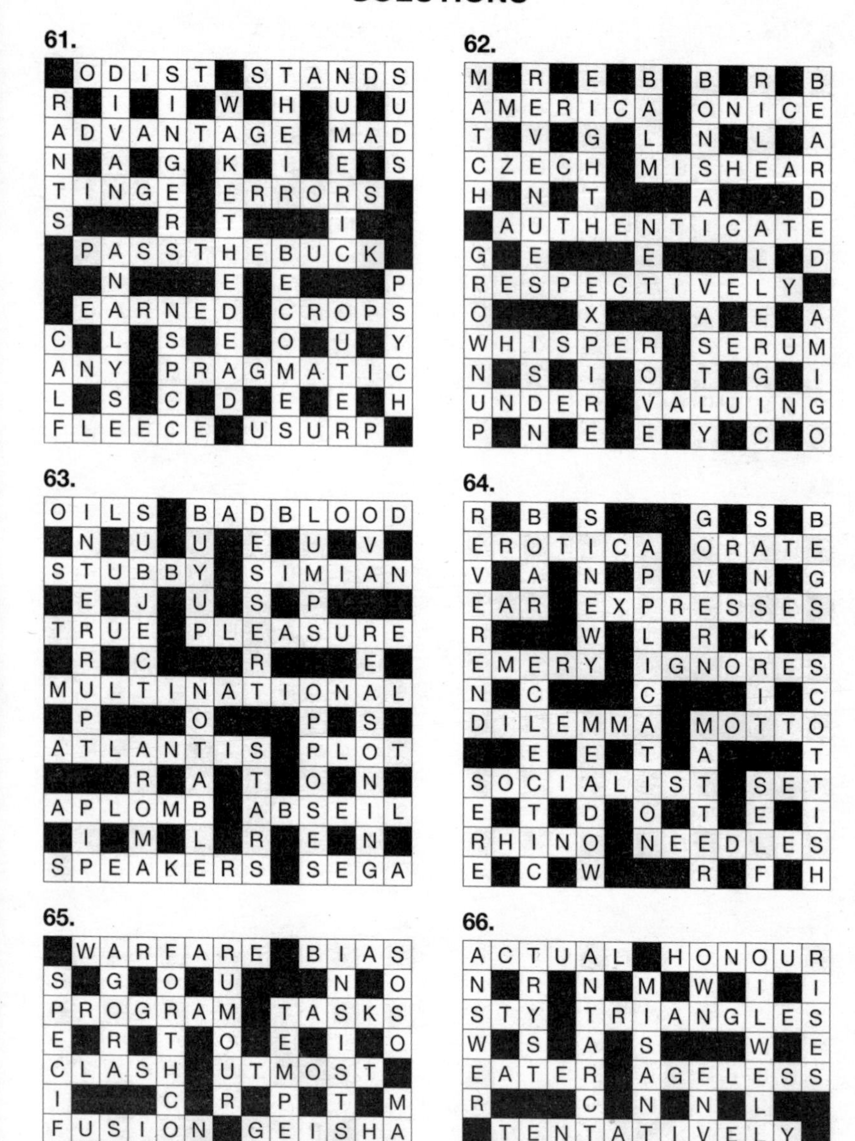

SOLUTIONS

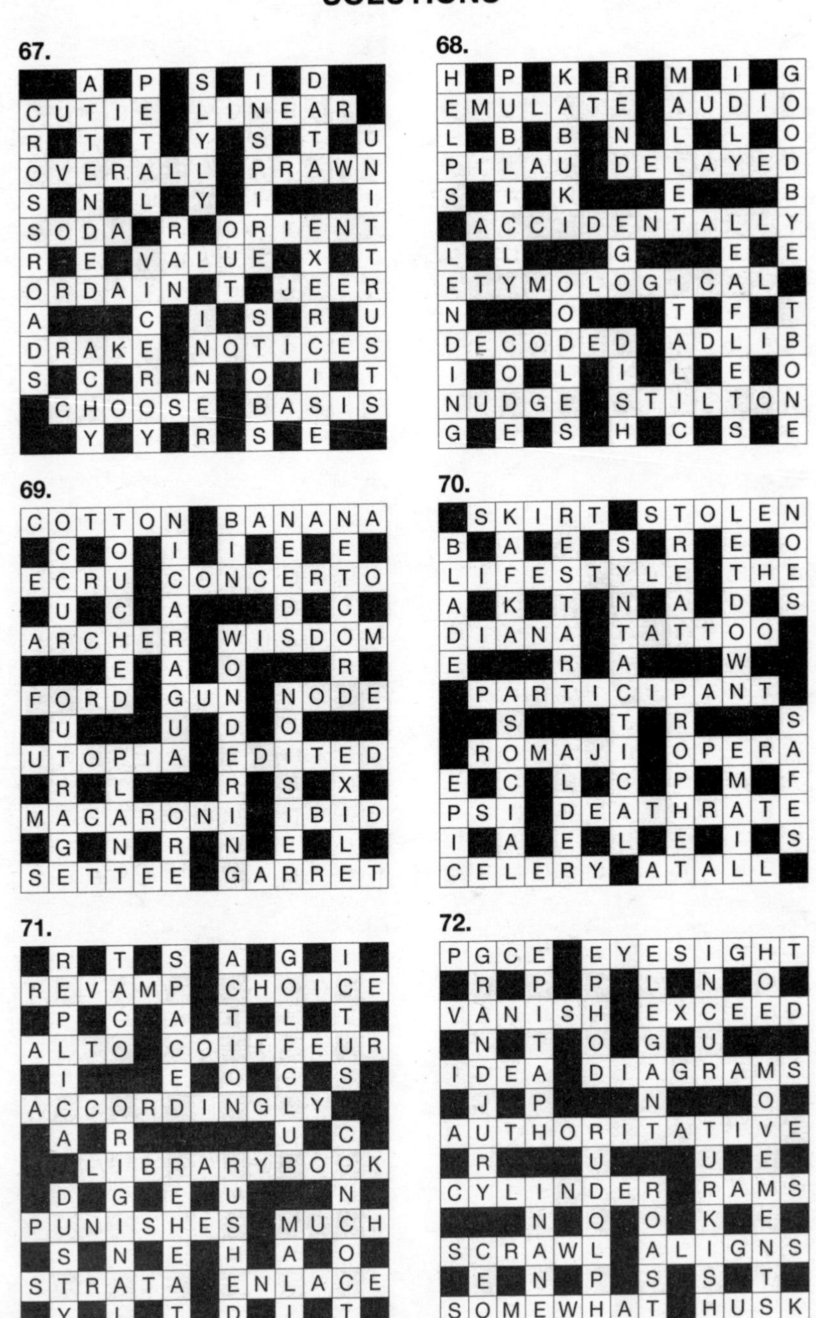

SOLUTIONS

73.

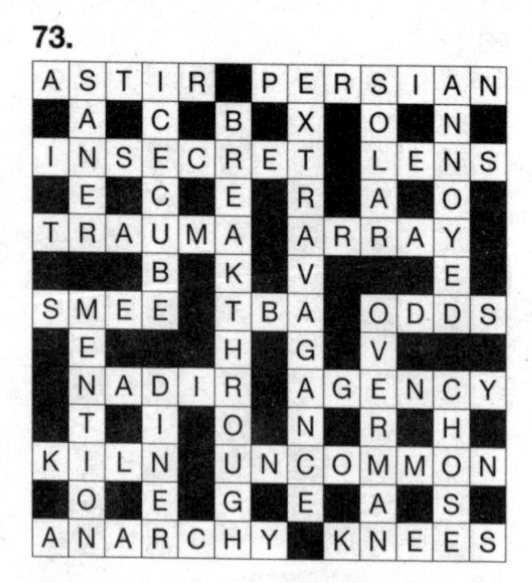

74.

A	R	M	A	D	A		T	A	S	T	E	S
	E		R		C		E		E		Q	
S	T	A	T		C	O	N	T	I	N	U	E
	R		I		O				Z		A	
H	O	N	S	H	U		G	U	E	S	T	S
			T		N		O				O	
U	F	O	S		T	W	O		E	A	R	S
	L				E		D		V			
W	A	R	P	E	D		G	L	O	W	E	D
	S		A				R		L		X	
S	H	A	N	G	H	A	I		V	I	C	E
	E		I		I		E		E		E	
E	D	U	C	E	D		F	I	D	D	L	E

75.

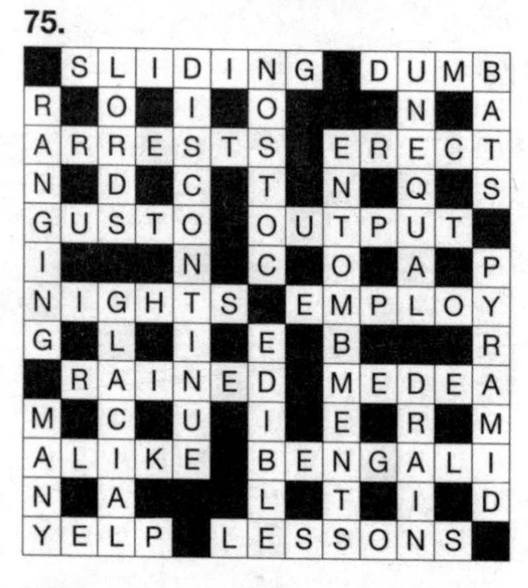

76.

77.

78.

C	O	E	F	F	I	C	I	E	N	T	S	
L		C		R		R		N		A		P
O	Z	O	N	E		A	N	T	E	N	N	A
C		N		D		Y		I				R
K	N	O	W		C	O	N	T	E	M	P	T
W		M		R		N		L		A		I
A	B	I	D	E	S		M	E	T	R	I	C
T		C		D		C		D		G		I
C	U	S	T	O	M	E	R		G	A	S	P
H				L		L		G		R		A
E	L	E	M	E	N	T		O	N	I	O	N
R		R		N		I		A		T		T
	C	R	I	T	I	C	A	L	M	A	S	S

SOLUTIONS

79.

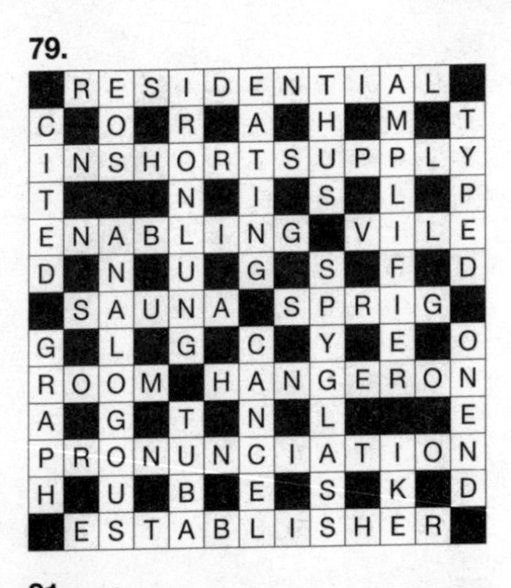

80.

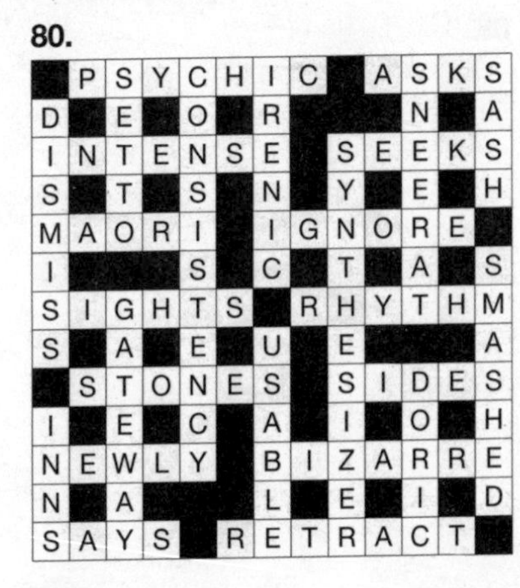

81.

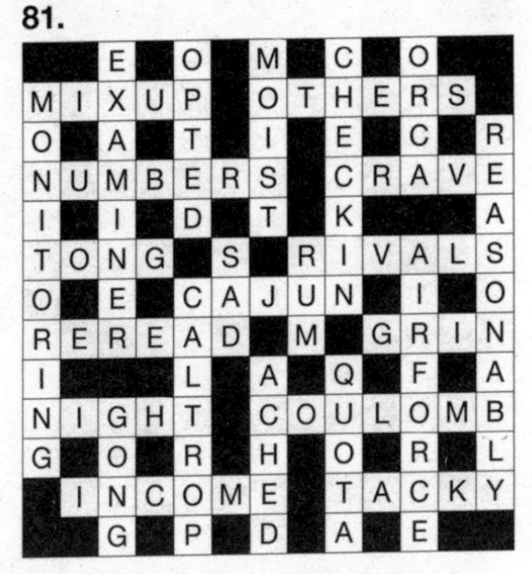

82.

83.

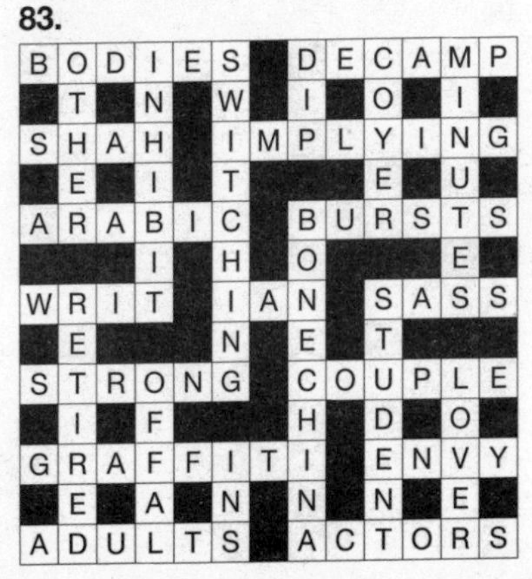

84.

SOLUTIONS

85.

86.

S		C		W		P		L		W		T
U	S	H	E	R		L	E	A	T	H	E	R
P		O		E		A		R		A		E
E	X	P	A	N	D	S		G	E	T	O	N
R		C				M		E				D
B	O	H	E	M	I	A	N	S		P	L	Y
		O		O				S		R		
O	A	P		L	I	S	T	E	N	I	N	G
B				E		T				N		O
L	U	D	I	C		R	O	T	A	T	E	S
I		I		U		E		O		O		L
G	O	R	I	L	L	A		P	L	U	T	O
E		T		E		M		S		T		W

87.

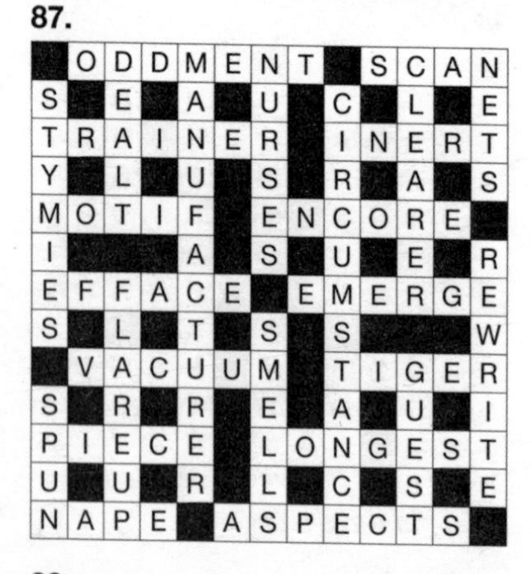

88.

S	P	E	E	D	S		B	E	R	T	H	A
T		L		U		N		M		R		V
U	T	D		P	H	E	N	O	M	E	N	A
F		E		L		U				A		I
F	A	R	S	I		R	A	D	I	C	A	L
S				C		O		I		L		
	E	S	T	A	B	L	I	S	H	E	S	
		W		T		O		C				B
I	C	E	B	E	R	G		U	N	I	T	Y
R		A				I		S		M		P
I	N	T	E	R	E	S	T	S		B	A	A
S		E		U		T		E		U		S
H	I	D	I	N	G		A	D	I	E	U	S

89.

90.

A	S	K	E	D		S	P	E	C	I	A	L
	T		X		M		R		O		C	
J	A	P	A	N	E	S	E		Y	A	C	K
	F		M		T		F		P		E	
A	F	R	I	C	A		E	Q	U	I	P	
			N		P		R				T	
M	E	R	E		H	U	E		R	E	S	T
	M				O		N		I			
	E	N	T	E	R		T	A	S	T	E	D
	R		H		I		I		O		A	
O	G	L	E		C	H	A	P	T	E	R	S
	E		C		A		L		T		T	
A	S	S	A	U	L	T		M	O	C	H	A

SOLUTIONS

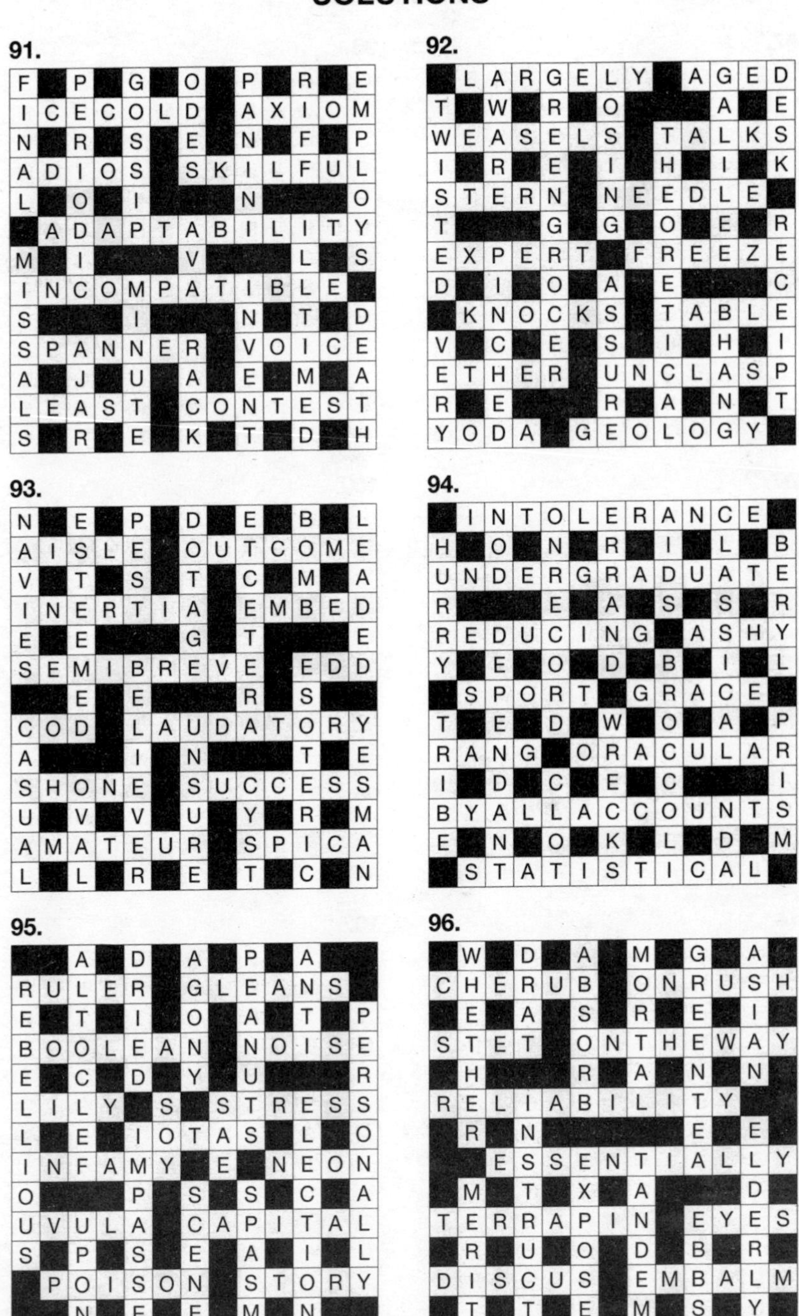

SOLUTIONS

97.

A	L	L	O	W	S		V	E	N	D	E	D
P		A		O		O		C		E		R
A	Y	R		R	A	U	C	O	U	S	L	Y
T		V		L		T				E		A
H	E	A	R	D		O	R	D	E	R	E	D
Y				W		F		E		V		
	M	I	L	I	T	A	N	C	I	E	S	
		L		D		C		R				S
U	G	L	I	E	S	T		E	G	R	E	T
N		E				I		A		A		R
I	N	G	E	N	I	O	U	S		B	P	I
T		A		C		N		E		B		N
S	A	L	M	O	N		A	S	K	I	N	G

98.

C		S		F		S		M		Z		E
L	U	C	R	E		O	N	E	N	E	S	S
E		H		E		M		T		S		C
V	A	N	I	L	L	A		A	S	T	E	R
E		A				L		P				O
R	E	P	U	B	L	I	S	H		T	O	W
		P		U				O		O		
A	B	S		M	I	S	E	R	A	B	L	E
N				P		A				O		V
G	E	N	I	I		F	A	T	I	G	U	E
E		O		N		A		E		G		N
L	O	B	S	T	E	R		C	H	A	S	E
S		S		O		I		H		N		D

99.

A	T	T	E	N	D		D	R	I	V	E	N
	R		C		E		J		D		X	
W	A	L	L		D	I	S	L	I	K	E	D
	I		I		U				O		C	
O	N	S	P	E	C		F	A	M	O	U	S
			S		T		A				T	
E	P	E	E		I	O	N		E	W	E	S
	R				O		T		M			
R	E	T	A	I	N		A	B	O	R	T	S
	S		F				S		T		A	
R	E	S	T	R	I	C	T		I	C	K	Y
	N		E		R		I		O		E	
S	T	A	R	E	S		C	A	N	A	R	Y

100.

S	P	O	O	L		R	E	A	S	O	N	S
	I		N		H		A		H		U	
E	L	E	P	H	A	N	T		R	O	M	A
	O		A		N		H		U		E	
S	T	U	P	I	D		U	M	B	E	R	
			E		K		M				A	
H	A	I	R		E	B	B		L	U	L	L
	V				R		L		A			
	E	T	H	I	C		E	X	T	R	A	S
	R		E		H		P		T		T	
T	A	X	I		I	N	I	T	I	A	L	S
	G		S		E		E		C		A	
R	E	C	T	I	F	Y		V	E	R	S	E

101.

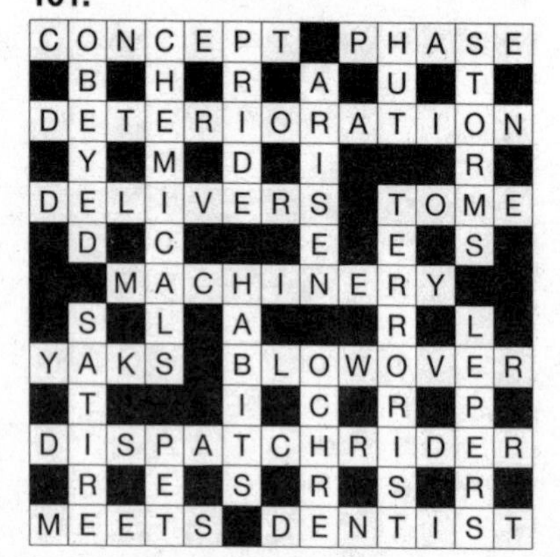

C	O	N	C	E	P	T		P	H	A	S	E
	B		H		R		A		U		T	
D	E	T	E	R	I	O	R	A	T	I	O	N
	Y		M		D		I				R	
D	E	L	I	V	E	R	S		T	O	M	E
	D		C				E		E		S	
		M	A	C	H	I	N	E	R	Y		
	S		L		A				R		L	
Y	A	K	S		B	L	O	W	O	V	E	R
	T				I		C		R		P	
D	I	S	P	A	T	C	H	R	I	D	E	R
	R		E		S		R		S		R	
M	E	E	T	S		D	E	N	T	I	S	T

102.

T	R	I	A	L	S		S	T	A	G	E	S
U		N		E				E		I		H
N	U	T		F	O	R	E	T	A	S	T	E
N		R		T		E		R				E
E	M	I	R		C	L	E	A	R	C	U	T
L		N		G		A		R		O		S
		S	C	E	P	T	I	C	A	L		
O		I		N		I		H		L		I
B	A	C	H	E	L	O	R		H	A	R	M
T				R		N		F		P		B
A	P	P	R	A	I	S	A	L		S	K	I
I		H		T				E		E		B
N	A	I	V	E	R		P	A	D	D	L	E

SOLUTIONS

103.

104.

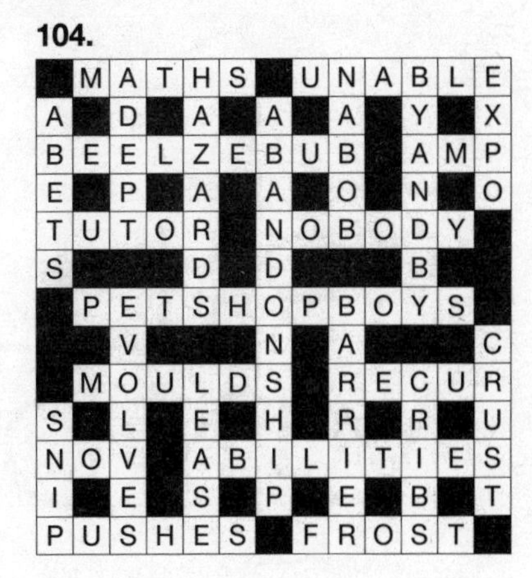